72-HOUR FAMILY
EMERGENCY
PREPAREDNESS CHECKLIST ✓

"PREPARE EVERY NEEDFUL THING"

BARRY G. CROCKETT, M.H.Ed.
LYNETTE B. CROCKETT

An urgent, practical, and simple guide
to help you and your family
prepare in advance for emergencies
which may require evacuation.

Barry Crockett holds an Associate of Applied Science Degree in Mobile Emergency Care (Paramedic) from Weber State College, a Bachelors Degree in Communications, and a Masters Degree in Health Education, both from Brigham Young University. Lynette Crockett attended Brigham Young University and Utah Valley Community College and is a mother and homemaker.

© Copyright 1983, 1989
by Barry G. & Lynette B. Crockett
All rights reserved.
Library of Congress Catalog Card Number 83-73117
ISBN: 0-915131-06-4

Ninth Printing October 1989

Publishers Press, Salt Lake City, Utah

Additional copies may be ordered at $7.95 each plus
$1.00 postage and handling to:
Barry Crockett
P.O. Box 1601
Orem, Utah 84057

For information on quantity discounts,
call (801) 225-8873.

CONTENTS

The nature of most emergencies for which we should prepare will not permit us the luxury of going around the house to gather items which may be needed. *Photo courtesy American Red Cross.*

OBJECTIVE

The security of you and your family is a top priority. People spend literally hundreds of dollars annually in premiums to insure for the unexpected. However, very few people take precautions ahead of time which can preserve their safety before, during and after an emergency situation. For the price of a couple of insurance premiums you can assemble or purchase a well organized Emergency Preparedness Kit.

The objective of the Family Emergency Preparedness Kit is to have, in one location, all of those essential items your family will require during a 72-hour period following an emergency. Survival in this modern day and age is generally a short-term situation. Seventy-two hours is usually the maximum amount of time it would take local, state, or if needed, federal emergency relief crews and supplies to arrive at virtually any given location.

Accidents, fires, floods and earthquakes take a daily toll of life and property in the United States, as is readily evident on the nightly news. Resulting turmoil and chaos usually place limitations upon the transportation and delivery of goods and services which may force you to move your family to a safer or more secure location.

The seriousness of your situation will, of course, depend upon the type of weather, your family's physical condition, and the resources at hand. The success or failure will depend upon your family's ability to adapt to the emergency and solve the problem of providing the necessities of life: air, water, shelter, warmth and energy long enough to get yourself out of the predicament, or long enough for others to bring those necessities to you.

Statisticians are gloomy about survival odds under crisis or severe emergency conditions. However, the worst part may not be the disaster itself. Often, the disaster's aftermath takes the largest toll on life and health. Lack of clean water, food, heat, light, first aid equipment and trained medical help, or in other words, the lack of preparation and not the disaster itself, is usually the killer.

Ideally, we would like to know the time and nature of an emergency or crisis situation. This would allow us to make advanced preparations and feel somewhat secure when the event actually takes place. In reality this is never the case. The nature of most emergencies for which we should prepare will not permit us the luxury of going around the house gathering up items which may be needed.

Emphasis on this subject is not grounds for panic or crisis thinking. On the contrary, personal and family preparedness for the unexpected should be a way of provident living and a matter of common sense.

DIRECTIONS

Your Family Emergency Preparedness Kit will need to be individualized according to your personal needs and your family situation. Be sure to keep in mind such things as your family size, your climate, and potential emergency situations akin to your area, such as flooding or earthquakes. Try to project possible needs under various emergency conditions. Also, consider the health and age of each family member. It may limit how much that individual is able to carry or pack with him. Don't necessarily count on having a car to pack everything around in during an emergency situation.

Plan to carry warmth, energy and shelter in your pack or kit. You must be self-sufficient. The home in your pack must be adequate and include (figuratively speaking) a kitchen sink, medicine chest, bathroom and clothes closet.

Following is a very comprehensive and definitive list of every possible item you may want to have with you in an emergency. They are listed under several distinct categories. **A star ★ is placed by those essential items which are strongly suggested. Be sure to include those items.** The remainder of the items to include are up to your family. Be very selective. Keep a critical eye for unnecessary accessories. Using a high-lighter, choose only those items you think you will need. "Extras" only add extra weight and will be burdensome.

Start immediately to obtain the items on your list. You will be surprised how quickly and inexpensively you can obtain most of the items you wish to include. Your local sporting goods stores, army surplus stores, and home centers are excellent sources for several items on the list. Check items off the list as you obtain them. Set a family goal to acquire a few high priority items every payday or whenever you get a few extra dollars.

Obviously your family might never experience a catastrophic disaster that will pit your family's lives against your preparation and ingenuity. Nevertheless, being prepared with a fully stocked Family Emergency Preparedness Kit will permit you and your family to cast aside some of the fears of an uncertain future and feel confident in an emergency situation. It may even save your life or that of a loved one. Good luck!

Devastating floods take place in nearly every part of the United States, resulting in loss of life and property. Here, a Coast Guard rescue helicopter, center right, searches for stranded and hurt victims.

Hurricane Agnes, Pennsylvania, 1972. *Photo courtesy U.S. Coast Guard.*

HELPFUL SUGGESTIONS & REMINDERS

- **IMPORTANT: Your Family Emergency Preparedness Kit(s) should be placed in a location that is safe, convenient and known to all members of your family, where it can be picked up quickly at a moment's notice, preferably near an exit on the ground floor or near a window. The location should be cool, dry and dark if possible.**

- **Nearby for easy access should be a waterproof packet containing the most valuable of the family's personal documents, such as genealogical records, priceless photographs, etc.**

- You may want to provide a self-sustaining emergency preparedness kit or backpack for each individual member of the family old enough to carry one.

- All items or groups of items should be placed in Zip-loc plastic bags. These are waterproof and air tight. These will help prevent a liquid item from spilling and ruining other items in your kit.

- You may want to color code various sections of your kit.

- Make a laminated master list of your kit's contents and location of various items and attach this list to the outside of your kit.

- Label each container such as sanitation, first aid, etc.

- Include instructions for the use of each item.

- **Make an "if time and room allows" list of last minute items to include posted near an exit or attached to your kit.** You may want to include precious items such as heirlooms, paintings, souvenirs or collections. These can be placed in your car if room allows.

- Re-evaluate your family needs and update your kit at least once a year (new children, etc.).

- Try not to include glass bottles of any type. They only add more weight and are breakable.

- Never carry anything in the hands that can be toted on the back. This frees your hands to carry small children, etc.

- **Have a predetermined action plan and an alternate plan to re-unite your family at a central location or meeting point in the event of family separation in an emergency.** Go over the plan many times with your family. Doing this will save lots of anxiety and worry.

- Find out how many feet your property is above or below possible flood levels so when predicted flood levels are broadcast, you can determine if you may be flooded.

- **Each member of the family should know how to turn off your home's gas, water, and electricity.**

- **Take lessons and become proficient in first aid.** (Red Cross classes are generally free.)

- Produce as much as possible through sewing, making household items, and gardening (makes an excellent emergency food supply).

- Learn techniques of home canning, freezing, and drying of foods (for greater self-reliance).

- **Store and save at least a one-year supply of food, clothing, and if possible fuel, such as wood or coal, and a two-week supply of safe drinking water.** (Fifty gallon plastic industrial-type barrels with a plastic siphon are excellent for storing water.) A year's supply of goods will help provide for non-evacuation emergencies such as financial stress, loss of employment, food shortages caused by truck strikes, adverse weather conditions, etc. Also, having a year's supply allows you the flexibility to wait for good sales through the year to re-stock, thereby saving you considerable money.

- Check your home food storage at least once a month, rotating for kitchen use regularly. Food storage should be kept in a dark, cool and dry location of your home.

- **Don't count on having a car, a functioning gas station, or accessible roads to leave an emergency area.** Emergencies may occur on holidays, weekends or perhaps in the middle of the night when gas stations are not likely to be open. Gas pumps do not function without electricity, which is usually the first service to be disrupted in a disaster.

- Get copies of good basic survival literature and become familiar with the survival advice contained in it.

- **A smaller, miniature version of your Emergency Preparedness Kit should be placed in the trunk of your car for long trips.**

- You may want to line your backpack with one or two large, strong trash can liners before placing the small Zip-loc bags of items in the backpack. This way the entire contents can be easily taken out and slipped back in your backpack, allowing you to use the backpack for summer camping trips, etc. This will also help to further waterproof your items.

- If possible, try to obtain small trial size or sample size plastic containers of various items you may need.

- Shop around and compare prices. Take advantage of good sales on items that you need.

- You may want to test your preparedness kit by going camping with it for 72 hours.

- Try to avoid expensive or exotic items. Instead, use ordinary, everyday items wherever possible. You can upgrade your kit when your budget allows.

- Make an effort to pool your resources with those of neighbors, friends, family and relatives to assemble supplies economically.

- **Remember individuals with special needs such as infants, toddlers, invalids, the ill, the blind, the handicapped and the elderly.**

- **Keep a waterproof first aid kit and flashlight in your home and car at all times.**

- You should have a definite plan for responding to an emergency. **Teach your family how to respond to disasters most likely to happen in your area** and be familiar with disaster plans of local organizations such as the Civil Defense and Red Cross.

- Learn your community's audible warning signals. You should find out now, before any emergency occurs, what warning signals are being used in your community, what they sound like, what they mean, and what actions you should take when you hear them.

- Identify local and national relief sources.

- All families should obtain and review civil defense manuals. Information about shelters, evacuation plans, medical supplies and fallout meters are available from state Civil Defense authorities.

- **The family should discuss orderly and efficient evacuation of their home** so that if a disaster occurs, they will be prepared to evacuate immediately.

- **Each family member should know where to go, what to take and for whom he or she is responsible, such as a younger brother or sister.**

- **Each family member should know how to contact** community emergency resources if communication is possible such as **police, fire, paramedics, etc.**

- Under stress man is at the mercy of the mind. Fears may well be responsible for more deaths than exposure, hunger or other damage. Fear and imagination plague almost every person who is face to face with a crisis. Realizing you have fears and that these are normal emotions in unfamiliar situations, you will be aware of them and better able to cope with them as they appear. Fears can be expected in any outdoor problem situation. Fear of the unknown and fear of your ability to cope with the situation will be foremost, along with a fear of being alone, animals, darkness, suffering, or death. Fear is usually based on lack of self-confidence and lack of adequate preparation. Knowledge and experience (practice sessions) will help to instill confidence and help to control fear.

- Inform yourself of the existence and location of shelters in your area. **Locate the public shelter nearest your home, work or school.**

- Have a list of items in your kit with dates to replace or inspect certain items, especially foods, outgrown clothing and medications.

- Being prepared will enable you to reach out and help others in crisis situations, such as a handicapped or elderly neighbor.

- Make a label to be sewn or attached to the outside of your kit using an indelible marker or pen. You may want to include the following, especially on children's kits:
    - Name
    - Name of parents
    - Home address
    - Phone number
    - Birthdate
    - The person to notify in an emergency
    - Names of relatives, close friends or neighbors (in case individual is lost, separated or injured)

    _____
    _____
    _____
    _____
    _____
    _____
    _____

    - Blood type/Rh factor (ask your doctor)
    - Allergies
    - Medications currently taking with any special instructions
    - Medic-alert tag or card (if applicable)
    - Other pertinant medical history or information
    - "Vial of Life" information

CONTAINER

This item is very important. Having a container that is well organized makes for easy access of any item during a frantic moment. Periodic inventory is also easily accomplished when the contents of the kit are laid out in an orderly fashion.

Containers must be waterproof, have some type of a carrying handle, and must be able to be carried easily by family members. **A star ★ by an item indicates that it is essential or strongly suggested.**

★ ☐ **Backpacks** (most preferable) — Must be of a large size, of waterproof nylon, lightweight aluminum frame, and padded shoulder straps. Try to include the absolute essentials in your backpack and put optional or additional items in other containers. Then, if you're not able to use your car to carry additional equipment, at least you will have the absolute essentials. Available at sporting goods stores.

☐ Beltpacks (with or without pockets) — Waterproof nylon. This item goes around the waist to hold additional items.

☐ Suitcases — Must be waterproof and sturdy, with a padded carrying handle.

☐ Polyethylene Plastic Buckets — Must have sturdy, padded handles, and tight fitting lids. These are available in four, five, or six gallon capacity.

☐ Duffle Bags — Must be of waterproof nylon.

☐ Tote Bags — Must be of waterproof nylon.

☐ Rucksack — Waterproof nylon.

☐ Briefcases — Must be waterproof with sturdy, padded handle.

☐ Trunk or Footlocker — Must be sturdy and waterproof with a strong, padded handle. They are great for placing in your car; however, they are very difficult to carry when full.

☐ Ammunition Boxes (Army surplus type) — These are made of heavy metal. They are waterproof and are available in various sizes; however, they are heavy and may be somewhat difficult to carry.

☐ Large Plastic Garbage Container — Very difficult to carry when full; however, they are great to collect your items in.

An adequate supply of fresh water in a clean container is the single most important element of emergency preparedness supplies. *Photo near Sundance Ski Resort, Provo, Utah.*

WATER

Water is the single most important item. Allow at least one (1) gallon per person per day and no less than that. This is absolutely essential. The body can live without food for extended periods of time but can live only for about three or four days without water. This is not considering stressful or emergency situations.

- The human body is approximately 80 percent liquids. Intake and output of liquids are necessary to the processes of life and the normal functions of the vital organs. When water loss exceeds intake, dehydration takes place. Dehydration of six percent to eight percent of the body weight will result in decreased body efficiency. Uncorrected, it will end in complete collapse and death.

- Humans lose water three ways: perspiration, breathing, and urination. We lose about one gallon per day in the summer. Adequate salt intake helps retain water in our body system.

- For a person whose water supply is limited, the problem is to ration water losses rather than intake of water. Conserve the water in the body by reducing the body's basic needs for water. **Drink available water until your thirst is satisfied, instead of attempting to stretch the supply.** Try to avoid loss of body water through wind dehydration and sweating. Stay in the shade and wear clothing even if uncomfortable.

- Your emergency water will be used not only for drinking but also for dishwashing, brushing teeth, and for sponge or towel baths.

- **Be sure family members know where to find safe water, how to purify water, and how to turn off the water supply to your home.** Rotate or replace your water supply quarterly. **Items starred ★ are essential or strongly suggested.**

★ ☐ **Five-Gallon (approximately) Plastic Water Containers with Carrying Handle** (such as Reliance brand)—Change water four times per year. Keep the containers filled to the very top to avoid air. Available at sporting goods stores.

★ ☐ **Water Canteens (plastic) with Cloth Covers**—One canteen per person. Keep them filled to the top and change the water four times per year. Available at sporting goods stores.

- ☐ Water can also be carried in any sturdy, lightweight plastic container with a tight fitting lid, such as milk, soda pop, or refrigerator water containers.

★ ☐ **Iodine Water Purification Tablets (one bottle)**—Available at sporting goods stores.

★ ☐ **Halazone Water Purification Tablets (one bottle)**—Available at sporting goods stores.

☐ Liquid Chlorine Bleach for Water Purification (small, leakproof container)—Change the bleach twice per year.

☐ Pocket Purifier Drinking Straw for Water Purification—These are rather expensive.

- Remember that the safest way to purify questionable water is to bring it to a boil for five to ten minutes. Nevertheless, be sure to include in your kit any one of the above mentioned four items to purify water.

★ ☐ **Clear Plastic, 6 Feet by 6 Feet**—Used to construct a water (solar) still which will yield up to three pints of water per day per still. (Refer to *Boy Scout Fieldbook* for description, illustration, and instructions for use of a water or solar still.) Clear plastic can also be used to collect rain water. Clear plastic is available at home centers.

- Rain, caught in clean containers, is drinkable without purification. To collect rain water, spread out a plastic sheet, blankets, or cloth over sticks or limbs about 6 inches high above the ground. Create a sag so the water will be funneled to a low spot where a clean container can catch the rain water. You can also put out pans, shells, coconut shells, sails, awnings, bailing scoops, hubcaps, or wring rain water from clothing, towels or blankets. Other sources of water include snow, ice, dew, succulent plants, cactus, desert plants, ground water, waterholes, sap of trees and vines, and fruit. Domestic sources of water include water in a waterbed, toilet tank, and water heater.

★ ☐ **Vinyl Surgical Tubing, 4 Feet Long** (used to construct a water [solar] still) — Available at home centers.

★ ☐ **Salt Tablets (one bottle)** — Helps prevent dehydration. Available at sporting goods stores.

☐ Collapsible Plastic Drinking Cups. One per person.

☐ Collapsible Plastic or Canvas Waterpail with a Spigot. (You could collect and purify water in this system.)

☐ Aluminum Can (approximately #10 size) with Wire Handle — Used to boil water in.

☐ Soft Plastic Drinking Cups. One per person.

☐ Stainless Steel Drinking Cups. One per person. Doubles for cooking.

☐ Plastic Bag — Will carry and store water. (Dig a small hole in the ground to hold the bag upright.)

☐ De-salter Kit — Takes the salt out of sea water.

☐ Washcloth, Towel, or Old Pair of Nylons — Will act as a water strainer.

Swift water is extremely dangerous and demands utmost caution and avoidance if possible. Here, emergency workers reinforce undermined dikes as surging flood waters rip through the center of a residential neighborhood.

Bountiful, Utah, 1983.

FOOD

Food would be priceless if it were badly needed in an emergency situation. **You should include in your kit a three-day supply of non-perishable food, preferably requiring no refrigeration, cooking or preparation. The food items should be compact and lightweight** such as freeze-dried foods (most preferable) in sealed packages or food items in small cans. Food could also be placed in assorted, lock top plastic pill containers available at your local pharmacy. These can hold up to one cup of food and are water tight.

- Your first priority should be to include the most nutritious and high calorie food items first. Make sure it is a well-balanced diet. Nutrition is important because in an emergency you will be under unexpected stress and fear, which depletes your body of vital nutrients very quickly. To sustain life for 24 hours it takes about 1700 calories with the body at rest at a comfortable (not cold) temperature. Stressful or emergency conditions, which are physically exhausting, can expend 4,000 to 6,000 calories.

- Keep in mind both the storage life and the nutritional life of the foods you put in your kit. A food's nutritional value will be gone long before it spoils. That is why it is important to rotate or replace your food items. Keeping a record will help you rotate or replace food items before they spoil.

- Since "one bad apple spoils the whole bushel," it's a good idea to place each food item, regardless of what it comes in, into a Zip-loc plastic bag also. Using a wax marking pen, write the date of purchase on each food item to help you determine when to rotate or replace it. Canned foods lose their maximum freshness after one year. Freeze-dried foods will stay fresh for ten to fifteen years provided they are nitrogen vacuum packed and are kept in a cool, dry location. Aim to keep your emergency kit (with your food in it) in a cool, dark, dry location between 40°F to 60°F.

- Take into account your family's food preferences, their eating habits, ages and state of health. It is of no use to include foods your family doesn't like or can't eat.

- Each family member's food should be individualized to their own needs. **Pay particular attention to the needs of infants, invalids, diabetics, the elderly and chronically ill, the handicapped, and also those family members who are allergic to certain foods.**

  A star ★ by an item indicates that it is essential or strongly suggested.

★ ☐ **Canned Meats** (small cans) — Such as:
  - ☐ Tuna Fish
  - ☐ Ham
  - ☐ Chicken
  - ☐ Turkey
  - ☐ Shrimp
  - ☐ Salmon
  - ☐ Sardines
  - ☐ Corned Beef (also Hash)
  - ☐ Vienna Sausages
  - ☐ Sandwich Meatloaf
  - ☐ Spam
  - ☐ Treet
  - ☐ Deviled Meats
  - ☐ Beef Stew
  - ☐ Pepperoni
  - ☐ Soybean Products

★ ☐ **Smoked or Dried Meats** (advantage: lightweight) — Such as:
  - ☐ Beef Jerky
  - ☐ Venison Jerky

★ ☐ **Canned or Freeze-Dried Vegetables** (freeze-dried are very lightweight) — Such as:
  - ☐ Potatoes (dehydrated also)
  - ☐ Peas
  - ☐ Corn
  - ☐ Asparagus
  - ☐ Pickles
  - ☐ Mushrooms
  - ☐ Carrots
  - ☐ Squash
  - ☐ Beets
  - ☐ Hominy
  - ☐ Green Beans

★ ☐ **Canned or Dried Fruits** (dried fruits are very lightweight) — Such as:
  - ☐ Pears
  - ☐ Peaches
  - ☐ Cherries
  - ☐ Tomatoes
  - ☐ Plums
  - ☐ Prunes
  - ☐ Apples
  - ☐ Berries
  - ☐ Mushrooms
  - ☐ Olives
  - ☐ Shreaded Coconut
  - ☐ Apricots
  - ☐ Fruit Cocktail
  - ☐ Grapefruit
  - ☐ Mandarin Oranges
  - ☐ Applesauce
  - ☐ Pineapples
  - ☐ Fruit Leather
  - ☐ Raisins (small boxes)

★ ☐ **Juices** — Canned (4 to 6 ounce types), powdered or crystal form (lightweight), such as:
  - ☐ Orange Juice
  - ☐ Tomato Juice
  - ☐ V-8 Juice
  - ☐ Grape Juice
  - ☐ Apple Juice
  - ☐ Cranberry Juice
  - ☐ Baby Strained Juices (if applicable)
  - ☐ Cran-apple Juice
  - ☐ Grapefruit Juice
  - ☐ Pineapple Juice
  - ☐ Plum Juice
  - ☐ Prune Juice
  - ☐ Apricot Nectar

☐ Other Beverages — Such as:
  - ☐ Canned Soda Pop
  - ☐ Canned Milk Infant/Adult
  - ☐ Condensed Milk
  - ☐ Non-fat Dry Milk, Instant or Regular (add water)
  - ☐ Malted Milk Tablets or Powder (add water)
  - ☐ Infant Formula, powder or concentrate (add water)
  - ☐ Infant Formula for Infants with Allergies (add water)
  - ☐ Tang (add water)
  - ☐ Kool-Aid, Nutra-Sweet type (add water)
  - ☐ Lemonade, instant type (add water)
  - ☐ Postum (add hot water)
  - ☐ Hot Chocolate Packets (add hot water)
  - ☐ Hershey's Syrup, small can to flavor dried milk
  - ☐ Drinks in Foiled Containers or "punch boxes" such as "Capri Sun" brand.
  - ☐ Gator-aid, helps replace sodium and potassium which the body loses during hot summer weather
  - ☐ Punch Concentrate (add water)
  - ☐ Punch Crystals (add water)
  - ☐ Hawaiian Punch
  - ☐ Herbal Teas
  - ☐ Sugar-free Beverages (if applicable)
  - ☐ Pre-sweetened Beverages

☐ Pastas — Such as:
  - ☐ Canned Lasagna
  - ☐ Dry Noodles (lightweight)
  - ☐ Ramen Instant Noodles (lightweight, add hot water)
  - ☐ Canned Spaghetti
  - ☐ Macaroni and Cheese Mix (box, add hot water)

☐ Spices — Such as:
  - ★ ☐ **Salt**
  - ★ ☐ **Pepper**
  - ☐ Seasoned Salt
  - ☐ Imitation Bacon Bits
  - ☐ Other Spices or Flavorings

☐ Herbs

☐ Soups — Such as:
  - ★ ☐ **Bouillon Cubes** (broth) — Beef or Chicken
  - ☐ Dried Soups, Lipton type (lightweight)
  - ☐ "Soup in a Cup" (lightweight, add hot water)
  - ☐ Freeze-dried Soups (lightweight, add hot water)

☐ Basics — Such as:
  - ☐ Backpacking Foods, freeze-dried
  - ☐ White granulated sugar
  - ★ ☐ **Sugar Cubes,** individually wrapped in plastic
  - ☐ Powdered Sugar
  - ☐ Brown Sugar
  - ☐ Molasses
  - ☐ Honey
  - ☐ Flour
  - ☐ Bisquick-type Flour Mix
  - ☐ Cornstarch
  - ☐ Baking Soda
  - ☐ Powdered Cheddar Cheese
  - ☐ Brown Gravy Mixes (add hot water)
  - ☐ Dried Whole Eggs (add water)
  - ☐ Powdered Butter (add water)
  - ☐ Baking Powder
  - ☐ Corn Meal
  - ☐ Vegetable Oil (small leakproof container)

☐ Grains and Legumes — Such as:
  - ☐ Dry Cereal (baby type)
  - ☐ Dry Cereal — Sugared (comes in small, one ounce, single serving type boxes)
  - ☐ Alfalfa Sprouts (seeds)
  - ☐ Mung Beans
  - ☐ Millet

- ☐ Soy Beans
- ☐ Navy Beans
- ☐ Pinto Beans
- ☐ Pork and Beans
- ☐ Instant Rice (Uncle Ben's converted type)
- ☐ Instant Cereal (such as Oatmeal in individual packets)
- ☐ Canned Chili
- ☐ Dehydrated Canned Yukon Biscuits
- ★ ☐ **Wheat Kernels**
- ★ ☐ **Snack and High-Energy Stress Foods** — Acts as a natural tranquilizer for a feeling of well being
  - ☐ Hard Candy
  - ☐ Life Savers
  - ☐ Suckers or Lollipops for the little ones
  - ☐ "Gum Balls" for the little ones
  - ☐ Stick Gum
  - ☐ M&M's
  - ☐ Other "Penny" Candy
  - ☐ Canned Pudding ("snack packs")
  - ☐ Hershey's Tropical Chocolate Bars (does not melt, stores well)
  - ☐ Cheese Spread such as Cheese Whiz
  - ★ ☐ **Peanut Butter**
  - ★ ☐ **Canned Nuts**
  - ☐ Gorp (mixture of nuts, raisins, dried fruit, etc.)
  - ☐ Quick Meal Energy Bars
  - ☐ Health Food Bars

- ☐ "Space Food Sticks"
- ☐ Popcorn Kernels
- ☐ Granola Bars
- ☐ Sunflower Seeds
- ☐ Marshmellows
- ☐ Vanilla Wafers
- ☐ Protein Wafers
- ☐ Animal Crackers for the little ones
- ☐ Graham Crackers
- ☐ Saltine Crackers
- ☐ Stoneground Wheat Saltine Crackers
- ☐ Wheat Thins
- ☐ Sugar Cookies
- ☐ Pretzels

- ☐ Other Miscellaneous Food Items — Such as:
  - ☐ Pemmican
  - ☐ C-rations
  - ☐ K-rations
  - ☐ Beef Stew (canned or freeze-dried)
  - ☐ Baby Foods, chopped or strained (if applicable)
  - ★ ☐ **Baby Vitamins,** liquid (if applicable)
  - ★ ☐ **Adult, Children's Vitamins/Minerals** (chewable tablets)
  - ☐ Invalid Food Supplies (if illness exists)
  - ☐ Diabetic Foods (if applicable)
  - ☐ Diet, Low Calorie Foods (if applicable)
  - ☐ Freeze-dried Casseroles (in cups)
  - ☐ Dry Pet Food (if applicable)

FOOD EQUIPMENT

Most of the food equipment you will need obviously depends on what foods you have chosen to take along. Review your food list and decide what equipment will be needed to prepare and consume the food. Also, you will need to consider whether to use disposable, one-time use items or the re-useable types.

A star ★ by an item indicates that it is essential or strongly suggested.

★ ☐ **Mess Kit**—Such as the Boy Scout type. Very compact. Includes an aluminum fry pan, a plate, a kettle with a lid, and a plastic drinking cup. Available at sporting goods stores or wherever Boy Scout materials are sold in your area.

★ ☐ **Metal Knife, Fork, and Spoon Utensil Set**—Such as the Boy Scout type. Comes in a plastic case and is available at sporting goods stores or Boy Scout retail outlets.

★ ☐ **Can Opener**—Regular or the very small G.I. type. Available at grocery stores. The G.I. type is available at Army surplus stores.

★ ☐ **Metal Folding Cook Stove and Fuel**—Uses Sterno fuel or compressed fuel tablets. Available at Army surplus or sporting goods stores.

★ ☐ **Heavy Duty Aluminum Foil**—For cooking purposes.

☐ Small Breakdown Fishing Rod and Reel—Available at sporting goods stores.

★ ☐ **Miniature Fishing Kit**—Hooks, weights, lures, flies, floaters, spinners, 25-pound test line, swivels, artificial bait, one-sided razor blade, and survival fishing instructions. Available at sporting goods stores.

☐ Plastic Drinking Cups—Re-useable.

☐ Stainless Steel or Aluminum Drinking Cups—Doubles for cooking purposes.

☐ Insulated Foam Cups

☐ Paper Cups—One-time use only

☐ Measuring Cup

☐ Measuring Spoon(s)

☐ Small Aluminum "Meat Pie" Tins—For cooking and eating purposes.

☐ Emergency Tin Can Stove—Made from a #10 or comparable tin can.

☐ Plastic Eating Utensils

☐ Plastic Bowls

☐ Paper Bowls

☐ Container—To warm up baby's milk bottle (if applicable).

☐ Insulated Thermos Container

☐ Plastic Plates—Re-useable, picnic type.

☐ Paper Plates—One-time use only.

☐ Small Plastic Funnel—For filling baby bottles and other uses.

☐ Plastic Baby Milk/Juice Bottles with lids, nipples, etc.

☐ Plastic baby bibs. Available free at fast food restaurants.

☐ Hot Pads

☐ Bottle Opener

☐ Paper Napkins

☐ Waxed Paper

☐ Clear Wrap—Such as Glad Wrap or Saran Wrap.

☐ Pancake Turner

☐ Barbecue Fork

☐ Large Spoon or Ladle

☐ Metal Grill for Cooking Meat

☐ Plastic 2-Quart Container with Lid

☐ Small Fishing Net

☐ Hank Roberts Mini Mark III Stove—Compact. Uses butane fuel. (Not as hot as white gas.)

☐ Backpacker's Stove and Fuel—Compact.

☐ "Blue Ice" Pack—A last minute item you may want to include. Lasts 72 hours. Colder than water ice. Excellent for hot weather, medical emergencies, and has multiple food uses.

☐ Small Picnic-type Tablecloth.

☐ Snare Wire—To trap small game.

☐ Rat Trap—Excellent for trapping small game.

☐ Rifle and Ammunition—For killing wild game.

Don't always count on having a car, functioning gas station, or accessible roads to leave an emergency area. Make sure you can get by at home a week or two in case a winter storm isolates you, and it's impossible for you to leave.

Adams, New York, 1977. *Photo courtesy National Oceanic and Atmospheric Administration.*

SHELTER

The objective of shelter is to provide emergency housing. It is extremely important to be physically protected from nature's weather elements such as the wind, cold, rain and sun. **Strange as it may seem, people in the cold outdoors can perish in a very short time without body shelter (in as little as three to six hours in extreme weather conditions, from the wind and cold).**

A person away from the comforts of home after evacuating is wholly dependent upon a limited supply of usable energy and the insulation qualities of the body shelter he wears or carries with him.

- Keep in mind your particular climate; however, **be prepared for the worst the elements and nature may have to offer.**

- The heat of the desert is just as deadly as the Arctic cold. The 1983 "heat wave" killed over 200 people across the nation.

- A car stalled in the country during a blizzard can be a major emergency. Help could be hours, even days away. In Arctic, or deep snow or blizzard conditions, a snow trench is the best shelter from wind and extreme cold. Snow is 32° insulation. Dip into hardened snowdrift and hollow out a small space with entrance lower than your feet. The temperature will soon climb to 15 to 20 degrees warmer than the outside temperature.

- Natural shelters include: logs, rocks, cliffs, underneath trees—any place with a lee side to protect the body from wind and rain. Timber is always a friendly shelter. It furnishes windbreaks and fire for warmth.

- **RAIN.** Cold and wetness cause extreme body heat loss. Keep as dry as possible, remain in a shelter. Keep fire wood dry, especially tinder for signal fires.

- **WIND.** Cools the body, blows away heat faster than the body can produce it. Cover all exposed parts of your body. Put on adequate clothing for body shelter or find a suitable natural shelter.

- **BLIZZARD.** Cold, heat loss, mobility threatened, causes mental stress. Do not travel. Quickly find suitable wind and cold shelter. Remain until storm abates. Gather lots of fire wood and boughs for insulation.

- **DENSE FOG, DARKNESS.** Loss of direction, mobility, heat loss, mental stress, fears, etc. Do not travel. Improvise adequate shelter, wait for daylight.

- **SUN, DESERT.** Body heat gain, dehydration, blindness, burns. Find shade or improvise shade. Do not travel in the heat of the day. Conserve energy. Set up a solar (water) still if you need water. Travel at night using the stars to navigate if on foot.

- **LIGHTNING.** Leave high, exposed areas immediately. Crouch down away from trees, caves, or cliffs. Stay in your car.

Starred ★ items are essential or strongly suggested.

★ ☐ **Family Tent** — Large enough for your entire family. Waterproof nylon, lightweight, compact. Available at sporting goods stores.

☐ Four-Man Back Backpacker's Nylon Tent — Waterproof, lightweight, compact.

★ ☐ **One-Man Pocket Emergency Tent** — Plastic. One per person. Available at sporting goods stores.

☐ Tent Pegs — Lightweight.

★ ☐ **Grommets** — Small doughnut-shaped fasteners which help prevent canvas or plastic from tearing when rope is tied through them. Available at sporting goods stores.

★ ☐ **Polyethelene Plastic** — Approximately ten feet by fifteen feet. An adequate shelter can be constructed from this material. It also can be used to construct a water "solar" still. Available at home centers.

☐ Umbrella

☐ Mosquito Netting — Shelter from insects.

☐ Extra Nylon — Fifteen yards. Waterproof. For shelter construction.

☐ Nylon Tarp

☐ Heavy Black Tarp — Shelter construction.

☐ Plastic Garbage Bags — Can serve as a rain poncho, groundcloth, "lean-to" or other shelter, or as a garbage container. Can also be cut and spread out to collect rainwater or used in constructing a "solar" water still.

☐ Leaf Bag — Seven bushel size fits a six foot man. Cut a hole in the sealed end for a face and head opening. Cover head if possible (not the face).

☐ Garbage Bag (30-gallon size) — Pull up over legs and tuck in pockets to protect legs from wind and rain. Can also be used for shade from the sun. Tape may be used to close the face opening and to secure the top and bottom plastic.

★ ☐ **Nylon Rope or Cord** (50 feet of ¼ inch) — For tying, hanging, or building purposes or can be used to construct a makeshift clothesline. Available at sporting goods stores.

★ ☐ **Duct Tape** (one small roll) — To repair tears in your shelter and to aid in shelter construction. Available at home centers.

☐ Emergency Blanket (aluminum coated mylar) — 56 inches by 84 inches. Great for shelter construction. Waterproof.

☐ Space Blankets with Grommets (82 inches by 50 inches) — Waterproof. Great for shelter construction.

☐ Small outdoor thermometer.

• A camper shell on top of a pick-up truck would be an excellent vehicle to consider evacuating in, with its built-in shelter and conveniences.

BEDDING

Bedding should be warm, lightweight, comfortable, waterproof and compact. Starred ★ items are essential or strongly suggested.

★ ☐ **Sleeping Bags—Lightweight, 2½ Pound Hollow-fill II,** with or without flannel insert. Very warm (rated 0°F to 10°F). Waterproof nylon covering. Place in a waterproof nylon or plastic bag. Hollow-fill II are the state-of-the-art in sleeping bags. The fibers in them are hollow, which greatly adds to its insulation qualities. This type of sleeping bag also dries out fast if it gets wet. Goose down bags, though warm, dry out slow when wet. The 2½ pound Hollow-fill II sleeping bags are available at sporting goods stores.

• Sleeping bags can be used also for shade from the sun, as a coat, as a "lean-to," and as a makeshift stretcher.

• Avoid sweating in your sleeping bag.

• Every morning, open the bag wide and air it out thoroughly.

• Use a poncho, trail pad (poly foam), or plastic ground cloth under the bag to protect it from ground moisture.

• Put insulation materials under the bag, as cold comes from below. Use inflatable sleeping pads, poly foam pads, cardboard, newspapers or boughs (tree branches), or bark.

• Fluff the sleeping bag thoroughly before using.

• Don't wear all your clothes in the bag.

• Place your outer garments *under* the sleeping bag and *over* your ground cloth (to keep them dry).

☐ Wool Blankets—Wool retains its warming properties even when wet. Can be used for sleeping, shade from sun, as a coat, and in the forming of a makeshift stretcher.

★ ☐ **Newspapers**—For insulation next to the ground.

☐ Poly Foam Trail Pads (sleeping pads)—For insulation from the ground. Lightweight and waterproof.

★ ☐ **Plastic Groundcloth**—Waterproof. Available at sporting goods stores.

☐ Clean White Sheet

☐ Small Rubberized Sheet—For infants and small children. Protects from bed wetting.

☐ Inflatable Air Mattresses—For added comfort. Can be used as a makeshift raft.

☐ Small Inflatable Pillow

☐ Large Trash Bags—Can be used as a groundcloth.

☐ Thermal Hospital Blankets

☐ Compact Nylon Hammock

★ ☐ **Space Blanket with Grommets**—Made from tough material evolved from insulation used in space exploration. It reflects 90% of your body heat back to you. Lightweight and waterproof. Size: 82 inches by 50 inches. Weight: 2½ ounces. Available at sporting goods stores.

★ ☐ **Emergency Blanket** (one per person)—Thinner and more compact (pocket size) and more lightweight than the space blanket. More for individual use. Size: 84 inches by 56 inches. Made from aluminum coated mylar. They can be used for sleeping, construction of a "solar" or water still, used as a coat, for shade from the sun, as a "lean-to," or for signaling. The space blanket (above) has similar uses. Available at sporting goods stores.

☐ Special Bedding for Invalids

Severe weather has increased the number of deaths and injuries dramatically in the last few years. *Photo courtesy National Oceanic and Atmospheric Administration.*

CLOTHING

Include in your kit one change of clothing and footwear for each member of the family, preferably work clothing. **Anticipate severe weather conditions.** Conserving your body heat is extremely important. If you have a growing family, update clothing sizes and needs at least once a year.

- Wear loose-fitting, lightweight, warm, easy-on easy-off clothing in several layers. This is more efficient than one or two layers of thick clothing. The layers can be removed to prevent perspiring and subsequent chilling.

- The outer garments should be wind and water repellent and have a hood. The hood should protect much of the face and cover the mouth to ensure warm breathing and protect the lungs from extremely cold air. This can also be done by breathing through a scarf.

- **The primary function of clothing is to retain a layer of radiated warm air (much like tropical air) close to the body.** Any cooler air passing the body tends to remove this warm air. The faster the wind (exchange of air), the greater the body heat loss.

- Clothing also has the function of protecting your largest organ, your skin (over 3,000 square inches) from the sun, cold, wind and rain.

- Exposure to wind, cold, or wetness may lower the body core (internal) temperature (98.6°F). This results in a condition known as hypothermia. This causes a rapid, progressive mental and physical collapse. During accidental lowering of the body temperature, the mind and thinking deteriorate, and muscle coordination declines. The body must be rewarmed, or the cold will continue to lower the body temperature until the vital organs fail.

- Radiation is the leading cause of heat loss. **An unprotected head may lose up to 50% of the body's total heat production at 40°F.** "If your feet are cold, put on a hat."

- Evaporation of sweat from the skin and respiratory moisture also contribute to heat loss. Inhaling cool air and exhaling warm air accounts for a significant heat loss.

- When the wind increases, even moderate temperatures become intolerable for body heat maintenance without proper clothing.

- **Wet clothing can extract heat from your body 240 times as fast as dry clothing. Wet clothing loses more than 90 percent of its insulation value.**

- **One can die from shivering in only two hours.**

- **Try to avoid wearing cottons.** Tight cotton clothing holds water next to the skin. Wet inner clothing causes freezing. Cotton clothing "wicks" (draws water up the very small individual fibers), thus retaining water.

- **Wool is a natural thermostatic insulator** that keeps you warm in the winter and cool in the summer. Wool is naturally durable and can withstand rugged and tough wear.

- **Wool clothing repels water and has the unique property of keeping the body warm even if it does get wet.** Wool dries from the inside out.

- In summary, to keep warm in cold weather, remember the word COLD:
    Clean wool clothing has open air spaces to hold warm air.
    Overheating—avoid perspiration. Wet clothing is cold.
    Layer system. Easy on-easy off layers of clothing to regulate body temperature.
    Dry. Keep dry. Dry wool clothing is your best insulation.

A star ★ by an item indicates that it is essential or strongly suggested.

- ★ ☐ **Hat for Sun Protection** — Such as baseball cap. Available at sporting goods stores.
- ★ ☐ **Knit Stocking Ski Cap** — With or without face mask. Available at sporting goods stores.
- ☐ Hat for Moisture Protection (wide-brimmed)
- ☐ Hard Hat
- ☐ Bandana
- ☐ Mosquito Head Nets — For insect protection
- ☐ Earbands or Earmuffs
- ☐ Scarf (winter neck type)
- ☐ Neckerchief — To protect neck from the sun
- ★ ☐ **Polarized Plastic Sunglasses and Case** — Available at grocery or sporting goods stores.
- ☐ Glacier Glasses
- ☐ Snow Goggles — To protect eyes from snow blindness.
- ☐ Plastic Eye Goggles — For eye protection.
- ★ ☐ **Mittens** (warmer than fingered gloves) — Available at sporting goods stores.
- ★ ☐ **Heavy-Duty Leather Work Gloves**
- ☐ Rubberized work gloves
- ☐ Cloth Gloves
- ★ ☐ **Extra Pair of Shoes** — For comfortable walking.
- ☐ Hiking Boots with Vibron or Lug Soles — For firm footing and ankle protection (worn in).
- ☐ Moon Boots — For snow and cold protection.
- ☐ Moccasins
- ☐ Rubber Boots or Overshoes (knee high) — For water protection.
- ☐ Rubber Hip Boots — For fishing and flood conditions.
- ☐ Leggings — For walking through wet fields, etc.
- ☐ Snow Shoes
- ☐ Ski Socks
- ☐ Regular Socks
- ★ ☐ **Heavy-Duty Wool Socks** (2 pairs per person) — Available at sporting goods stores.
- ☐ Rain Gear
- ★ ☐ **Two-Piece Rainsuit with Hood or Hat** — Treated waterproof nylon. These are more practical and comfortable for protection from rain than are ponchos. Available at sporting goods stores.

- ☐ Poncho with hood or hat (vinyl or plastic) — Waterproof. Can serve as a raincoat, a "lean-to," a rain collector, solar water still, or inflated as a raft.
- ☐ Large Trash Bags — Used for makeshift rain-gear. See Shelter section.
- ☐ Small Pocket Size Plastic Raincoat with Snaps
- ★ ☐ **Winter Coat** (polyfill insulation) — Dries out fast, warm.
- ☐ Winter Coat (goose down) — Dries out slow if wet. Winter coats should be waterproofed.
- ☐ Clothes from 60-40 Mountain Cloth (Gortex)
- ☐ Sweat Suit
- ☐ Wool Sweater
- ☐ Flannel or Wool Shirt
- ☐ Turtleneck Shirts/Sweaters (nylon or wool)
- ☐ T-shirt
- ☐ Long Pants (Levi-type and/or wool)
- ☐ Wool Undergarment
- ★ ☐ **Long Thermal Underwear** — Have a complete change of these. Available at sporting goods stores.
- ☐ Ski Underwear
- ☐ Other Undergarments
- ☐ Special Nursing Needs
- ★ ☐ **Large Bath Towel** (one per person)
- ☐ Handkerchief
- ☐ Leather Belt
- ☐ Extra Walking Cane (for elderly)
- ☐ Clothes Pins
- ☐ Leather Waterproofing Liquid (mink oil)
- ☐ Fabric Waterproofing Spray (silicone formula)
- ☐ Emergency Sustenance Vest — Available at Army surplus stores.
- ☐ G.I. Pistol Belt — To carry canteen, hunting knife, etc.
- ☐ Small Plastic Bags — Can be used for emergency waterproofing over socks in wet boots. Can be used as emergency gloves, or they can be used as waterproof, transparent containers for written messages.

With whirling winds of up to 300 miles an hour, tornadoes are the most violent of all atmospheric phenomena, and over a small area, the most destructive. They frequently accompany the advance of hurricanes. *Photo courtesy National Oceanic and Atmospheric Administration.*

FUEL

Electrical power and natural gas service to your home may be the first services interrupted during a natural disaster. Alternate fuel sources will be needed whether you evacuate from your home or are allowed to stay at home during the emergency. Fuel will be needed for keeping you and your family warm, dry and cheerful, for cooking, heating and purifying water, and for signaling. **Starred ★ items are essential or strong suggested.**

★ ☐ **Waterproofed Stick Matches** — Placed in plastic watertight containers (such as pill containers). Available at sporting goods stores.

☐ **"Hurricane" Matches** — Windproof.

☐ **"Metal Match"** — Waterproof, fireproof, durable, and non-toxic. Will light thousands of fires.

● Matches can be waterproofed with nail polish.

● Run a damp match rapidly through your hair several times to dry it.

★ ☐ **Fire Starters** — Approximately fifteen matches rolled tightly in corrugated cardboard, dipped in parafin wax, or a cube of wax-soaked insulating board, or a candle stubb, or paper egg cartons filled with wax and separated into cubicles. Wrap your fire starters in aluminum foil. Available commercially at sporting goods stores.

★ ☐ **Emergency Rescue Car Fuel** — Refer to the Car Equipment Section for a complete description.

☐ **"Fire Noodles** — Fire starters

☐ **Fire Starter Kit**

☐ **"Tinder Tabs"** — Fire starters

★ ☐ **Steel Wool** (grade 00, 000, or 0000) — Used for tinder. Hold 2 "D" flashlight cells together in one hand, while touching one end of a clump of steel wool to the very top of the top battery, while at the same time touching the other end of the clump of steel wool to the bottom end of the bottom battery. The current causes the steel wool fibers to incandesce and thus produce a flame. Steel wool can also be used to dry wood in order to start a fire. Available at grocery stores.

☐ **Cotton Balls** — For tinder.

☐ **Flint and Steel** — For starting fires. The most reliable "non-match" method of starting a fire.

★ ☐ **"Pink" Candles** — For warmth, light, and starting fires. These six-inch candles will burn four hours. Some are made to be smokeless and dripless. Available at sporting goods stores.

☐ **Small Camping or Utility Candles** — Avoid using the dinner-type candles.

☐ **Twin-Wick Canned Candle** — For long-term light and warmth.

☐ **Small, Lightweight Candle Holder.**

● White or light colored candles burn brighter than dark candles.

● Tallow candles burn brighter, longer, and are fairly smoke free when compared to wax candles.

☐ **Lighter** — Such as "Bic" for starting fires.

☐ **Small Magnifying Glass** — To start tinder on fire using the sun.

● Clear ice can be shaped into a lense that will start a fire, provided the sun is high and bright.

● Camera or binocular lenses or any convex lens such as the dome light glass in your car, can be a sun focusing fire starter if you don't have matches or a cigarette lighter in your car.

● Stuffing from the car seat makes good tinder to build a fire in an emergency.

● **A burning tire makes a hot fire that won't go out easily and lasts three to four hours.** Great for winter storm emergencies when you are stranded. It not only provides warmth but is also a good distress signal to bring help.

● If you have a live battery in your car, you can easily put sparks into tinder by attaching any wires to the posts and scaping the ends together in the tinder.

★ ☐ **Chemical Instant Heat Packs** — Approximately one to two hours of 110° heat. Available at medical supply companies.

☐ **"Wonder Warmer"** — Disposable heat. Lasts ten to twelve hours. Moderate heat. Not as hot as chemical packs (above).

★ ☐ **Portable Pocket Cooking Stoves** (folding type) — Available at sporting goods stores.

- ★ ☐ **Extra Heat Tablets (compressed fuel) for Pocket Stove** — Available at sporting goods stores.
- ★ ☐ **Sterno-Type Canned Fuel** — For cooking and warmth. Available at sporting goods stores.
- ☐ Small Backpacker's Stove and Fuel
- ☐ Hank Roberts Stove/Lantern — Uses butane fuel.
- ☐ Catalytic Safety Heater — Operates sixteen hours on a single filling. Available at Sears.
- ☐ White Gas
- ☐ Lantern Oil
- ☐ Butane Fuel
- ☐ Coleman Stove
- ☐ Charcoal Briquets — Adequate ventilation is a must to prevent carbon-monoxide poisoning.
- ☐ Pocket Handwarmer with Extra Fuel Sticks
- ☐ Tightly Rolled Newspapers — For fuel.
- ★ ☐ **Fire Extinguisher, Small Canister, ABC Type** — Available at home centers.
- • Look up for dry wood. Most trees have dead lower branches. These offer the driest firewood in rainy weather.

- • A fire on the snow will quickly disappear unless you have built a large green log base as an insulating platform to set your fire on.
- • Build several small fires around you for warmth instead of one big one.
- • The hood of your car can be removed and used as a heat reflector behind your fire.
- • **Carbon monoxide kills quietly. Ventillate closed quarters heated by any open flame heater, even a candle or lantern. Vent near the roof and the floor.**
- • **If you get stranded in cold weather or snow-bound, stay with your car. It's your best shelter. Run your engine and heater only ten minutes or so every hour.** You'll stay warm enough, and you'll be conserving gas in case you're stuck for a long time. When running your engine, **keep your window cracked for air** (on the opposite side of the car from which the wind is blowing). **Most importantly, make sure your tail pipe isn't covered with snow. Check it often.** If it is covered, deadly exhaust fumes could back up into your car. **Turn on your dome light occasionally** at night so you can see how other passengers are holding up. Also, **put out a distress flare** or colored balloons or flags so you'll be more easily seen.

LIGHT

Preparing alternate sources of light for use during emergencies or severe storms where the power may be knocked out is a must. Too many of us take light for granted because of its seemingly unlimited availability. One has only to be caught in a windowless shopping mall when the power goes out, or similar situation, to really appreciate its true worth. **Having the luxury of electrical power during an emergency or disaster is very unlikely.**

Wise planners will prepare in advance for alternate light sources to meet the "chilling blackness," which may very well accompany a disaster.

A star ★ by an item indicates that it is essential or strongly suggested.

★ ☐ **Waterproof Industrial-Type Heavy-Duty Flashlight**—Have available immediately. One per person. Available at sporting goods stores.

★ ☐ **Extra Alkaline Flashlight Batteries**—These will give about ten hours of continuous light. Check the batteries every three months.

★ ☐ **Extra Flashlight Bulbs**—The Krypton Star high-intensity flashlight lamp has about three times the brightness, range, and life of a standard flashlight bulb and is considered to be the best on the market.

☐ Battery-Powered Lanterns—Six or twelve volt. Will provide light for 24 to 86 hours.

☐ Flourescent Battery Lantern

☐ Backpacking Lantern—Compact, collapsible, lightweight. Uses liquid fuel.

★ ☐ **Cyalume Chemical Light Sticks**—Flameless, non-toxic, cool, windproof and waterproof. Contains two chemicals which activate when you bend the seven inch plastic tube, producing a luminous yellow-green light. The light will last eight to ten hours, the first thirty minutes being the brightest and most useful. Each person should carry two or three light sticks in their kit. Available at sporting goods stores.

☐ Coleman Lanterns

☐ Oil Lantern (a small one)

★ ☐ **Emergency Road Flares**—Available at auto parts stores.

☐ Small Propane Lamp and Fuel

☐ Small Gas Lantern Using White Gas

☐ Hank Roberts Lantern—Compact. Uses butane fuel.

☐ "Q-Beam" High Intensity Portable Light—plugs into cigarette lighter. Illuminates objects one mile away with its 200,000 candlepower.

● An emergency lantern can be made by filling a can or hubcap with sand or soil. Soak the soil with oil or gas from the car. You get gasoline from the car by using a heater hose as a siphon.

★ ☐ **Candles and Holders**—See Fuel section.

☐ Penlight Flashlight—Re-useable type.

☐ Generator Flashlight and Extra Bulbs—Requires no batteries. Electricity is generated by squeezing the grip lever.

● A good old-fashioned fire provides plenty of emergency light.

● **People are cautioned to be careful with non-electrical heat and light.** A fireplace or gas stove is better than space heaters which can be knocked over. Battery operated lights are preferable to lanterns or candles. **Problems can arise when people try to use camping stoves or lights in a closed room. That kind of equipment burns gas, and if the room isn't ventillated, the fumes will be extremely dangerous.**

Your best protection from a tornado is an underground shelter of a substantial steel-framed or reinforced concrete building.

Xenia, Ohio, 1974. *Photo courtesy Federal Emergency Management Agency.*

COMMUNICATIONS

Proper communications will be vitally important to you and your family's safety and well-being during an emergency or disaster. It will be your contact with the outside world. Not only will you need to be familiar with means to obtain special kinds of help your family may be in need of (medical, etc.), but you will also need means by which you can keep updated of emergency information from authorities in your area.

It is also helpful to have several different means of communication on hand to aid potential rescuers locate you or a member of your family if lost or stranded.

A star ★ is placed by those items which are essential or strongly suggested.

★ ☐ **Transistor Radio** (earphone optional) — Have available immediately. Might be your only link to the outside world. Know which is the Civil Defense radio station in your area. They have an emergency broadcast system which will broadcast important instructions to the public. Available at appliance stores.

★ ☐ **Extra Radio Batteries (alkaline)**

★ ☐ **Emergency Signal Flare** — Also serves as an excellent fire starter, distress signal, and device to signal oncoming traffic in case of auto accident or car problems.

☐ Smoke Signal — Red smoke, day-time signal. Smoke is the best day-time distress signal; fires are best at night. Available at Army surplus stores.

☐ Walkie-Talkies

☐ Emergency Strobe Light — Plugs into cigarette lighter. Excellent distress signal.

☐ 12-Gauge Red Meteor Flares — Shoots 200 feet into the air and has 10,000 candlepower.

☐ Aerial Flare — Shoots 400 feet up with 20,000 candlepower. Has a 20-mile visibility. Available at sporting goods stores.

★ ☐ **Stainless Steel Metal Mirror for Distress Signaling** — Available at sporting goods and Army surplus stores.

☐ CB Radio — Channel 9 is the emergency frequency.

☐ Police Scanner with State-wide Emergency Channel Crystal

☐ Small Notebook

☐ Pencil

☐ Pen

☐ Paper

☐ Envelopes

☐ Stamped Postcards — For emergency communication to relatives, etc., if phone systems are down.

☐ Several Postage Stamps

☐ Space Blanket or Emergency Blanket — Can be used for emergency signaling with their highly reflective surfaces. See section on Bedding.

☐ Reflectors (amber and red) — For highway problems and as a distress signal.

★ ☐ **Brass Whistles with String or Chain to Go Around Neck** — One per person. For distress signaling. The sound of a whistle will carry farther than the voice and will help save the voice. Available at sporting goods stores.

☐ Brightly Colored Cloth — Hung from the radio aerial or from a car window for use as a distress signal.

★ ☐ **Multi-Colored Balloons with String** — For use as a distress signal. Great for aerial searchers in locating a stranded car which has been snowed in or other similar situations.

★ ☐ **Mace or Riot Spray** — Check with your local police department as to where to obtain this item.

☐ "Scream" Emergency Sonic Alarm

☐ Emergency Signal Cards (laminated)

☐ Emergency Survival Cards (laminated)

● International emergency signal and survival cards are available by writing P.O. Box 805, Bloomington, Indiana 47401.

☐ Local Topographical Map — Shows you the shape of the land through printed elevation lines. A good map and its necessary companion, the compass, may save your life. Use your compass to orient the map so that it will line up with landmarks on the ground. Studying surrounding landmarks and map-indicated landmarks will usually put you back on the right track. Practice is necessary before this lifesaving tool can be relied on.

★ ☐ **Compass, Silva Filled**—Or Boy Scout type. For direction and orientation. Available at sporting goods stores or Boy Scout retail outlets.

★ ☐ **Road Maps or Atlas**—National, state, and local. Available at gas stations.

☐ Wrist Watch

★ ☐ **Small Personal Phone Book**—Of important names, addresses, and phone numbers with dimes and quarters attached for calling. For emergency communication purposes. These small blank phone books are available free from your telephone company.

- In time of disaster, don't use the telephone to get information or advice. Depend on radio or television.

- Write, telegraph, or telephone your relatives after the emergency is over so they will know you are safe. Otherwise, local authorities will waste time locating you—or if you have evacuated to a safer location, they may not be able to find you. (However, don't tie up the phone lines if they are still needed for official emergency calls.)

- Listed are various agencies, people, etc., you may want to include in your personal emergency phone book:

> Police
> Sheriff
> Highway Patrol
> Fire Department
> Ambulance
> Paramedics
> Rescue Squad
> Hospital Emergency Center
> Doctor (day and night numbers)
> Other Specialists (doctors)
> Dentist
> Pediatrician
> Physician's Information Service
> Emergency (dial 9-1-1)
> Operator (dial "0")
> Pharmacy (neighborhood)
> Pharmacy (24-hour service)

> Poison Control Center
> Burn Center
> Trauma Center
> Crisis Hotline
> Health Department
> Health Insurance Agent
> Other Insurance Agents
> Medicare Information Number
> Medicaid Information Number
> Road Conditions Number
> Taxi Cab
> Civil Defense
> Religious Leaders
> General Church Headquarters
> Church Welfare Services
> Close Family
> Relatives
> Neighbors
> Parents (at work)
> American Red Cross
> Search and Rescue
> Forest Service
> U.S. Coast Guard
> Gas Company
> Electric Company
> Water Company
> Automobile Club
> Amateur Radio Operator (name and call signal)
> Weather Bureau

- For night distress signaling, remove a headlamp from its housing and direct its beam upward in wide, sweeping arcs.

- A burning tire makes a hot fire and lots of easy-to-see thick black smoke which will provide an excellent distress signal for three to four hours.

- **A distress signal is three of anything, visual or audible, repeated at regular intervals. A distress signal answer is two of anything.**

- Your car horn can alert rescuers as far as a mile downward.

- There is a reservoir of oil under your car hood. A quart burned in a hubcap sends up a miniature cloud that is visible for miles.

- The lid of a can can be used to make a signaling mirror.

- Your car mirror can be used as a signaling device.

FIRST AID

It is most important to work on updating your first aid skills. The life or death of a family member may depend on your first aid abilities during a disaster. The American Red Cross offers classes in first aid and CPR which cost little or nothing. It's wise to take advantage of these classes. You can upgrade your first aid kit according to the training you have in first aid. **Include only items in your first aid kit you are familiar with and know how to use properly.**

A free brochure and price list of first aid items can be obtained by writing: Stat Medical Supply Company, Code (E), 4555 South 300 West, #300, Murray, Utah 84107. Telephone (801) 261-4363. Their merchandise is exceptional, and prices are very competitive.

- **All family members should know the basics: how to open the airway, mouth to mouth, CPR, and how to stop severe bleeding.**

- CPR stands for cardiopulmonary resuscitation. It's a technique used to get the heart and lungs working again once they've stopped.

- **Someone who has stopped breathing can die in four to six minutes. Serious brain damage can occur after just two or three minutes.**

- The basic objective is to rescue people whose lives are threatened, check for injuries and to provide emergency first aid.

- Adjust the size and quantity of your first aid kit to fit your needs.

- **Remember that medical facilities may be overloaded immediately after a severe disaster or crisis. Professional medical care may be unavailable for a long time.**

- The number of disaster victims requiring first aid treatment may be very large.

- Know where your medical supplies are located and how to get to them.

- **Each family member should have some basic first aid supplies in his/her own pack.** An enlarged family first aid supply in addition is wise.

- Individuals should become familiar with first aid manuals and supplies.

- **Each individual should be adequately immunized.**

- Each individual or family should carry adequate health insurance.

- **Remember items for persons with special needs** (such as diabetics, invalids, the handicapped, the elderly, those with chronic illnesses, etc.).

- **"Remember: You always have your most valuable equipment with you. The use of your hands and the breath of life in your lungs." (The American Trauma Society)**

    Starred ★ items are essential or strongly suggested.

- ★ ☐ **Sterile Dressings (Gauze) in Sealed Paper Packages** — Sizes 2x2 inches, 4x4 inches, 6x6 inches. For dressing cuts, burns, and lacerations.
- ★ ☐ **Telfa Non-Sticking Sterile Pads 4" x 4"** — Does not stick to the wound when bandaged
- ★ ☐ **Post-Op Sponges, 4" x 4"** — To control bleeding.
- ★ ☐ **Ace Bandages, 2 and 3 Inch Widths** — To hold dressings in place.
- ★ ☐ **Kerlix Gauze Rolls** — To cover wounds.
- ★ ☐ **Conforming Gauze Bandages** — For bandaging wounds.
- ★ ☐ **Sterile Oval Eye Pads** — To cover injured eyes.
- ★ ☐ **Muslin Triangular Bandages with Safety Pin** — For use as a bandage, tourniquet, or arm sling.
- ★ ☐ **Vaseline Gauze Dressing, Sterile** — For sucking chest wounds.
- ★ ☐ **Maternity or "OB" Pads** — To stop serious bleeding.
- ★ ☐ **Band-Aids, Various Sizes** — For minor wounds.
- ☐ Elastic Knuckle Bandages — For open wounds on the knuckle.
- ☐ Kerlix Sponges — To help control bleeding.
- ☐ Patient Bite Sponges — To control bleeding in mouth or teeth area.
- ☐ Fingertip Bandages
- ☐ Abdominal Pad, 9" x 5" — To control serious bleeding from a large wound.
- ☐ Compressed Gauze Bandages, 1" Wide — To hold dressings in place, help stop bleeding.
- ☐ Moleskin or Molefoam — For blister protection
- ☐ Cotton Absorbant Sponges, 2" x 2", 4" x 4" — To help control bleeding.
- ☐ Folded Sheet, Double Bed Size — Can be cut to make slings, bandages, etc.
- ● Bandages can be made from a white undershirt, handkerchiefs, or other cotton clothing in an emergency where ready-made materials are not available.
- ☐ 3M Steri-Strips — To close open wounds.
- ★ ☐ **Transpore Surgical Tape** (best type) — To hold bandages, dressings, and splints in place.
- ☐ Adhesive Tape — To hold dressings and splints in place.
- ☐ Micropore Paper Tape — To hold dressings and splints in place.
- ☐ Dermacell Cloth Tape, Hypo-Allergenic — To hold dressings and splints in place.
- ☐ Dermilite Paper Tape — To hold dressings and splints in place.
- ☐ Dermiform Knitted Silk Tape — To hold dressings and splints in place.
- ☐ Dermaform Cloth Tape, Hypo-Allergenic — For taping bandages and splints in place, especially good on very sensitive skin.
- ☐ Dermiclear Tape, Plastic, Transparent — To hold dressings and splints in place.
- ★ ☐ **Bandage-Type Scissors** — For cutting bandages, gauze, tape, etc.
- ★ ☐ **Tourniquet, Rubber or Velcro, 1" Wide** — To stop very severe bleeding.
- ☐ Constriction Band Made from Rubber Surgical Tubing — For bites and stings.
- ☐ Umbilical Clamps (2) — For emergency childbirth.
- ☐ Hemostatic Curved Forceps — For control of exposed vessel bleeding.
- ☐ 3-0, 5-0 Sutures — To close up open wounds.
- ☐ Large Extrication (Cervical) Collar — Foam with Velcro type, to help immobilize a possibly fractured neck.
- ★ ☐ **Medium Extrication (Cervical) Collar**
- ☐ Small Extrication (Cervical) Collar
- ★ ☐ **Assorted Sizes of Splints** — To immobilize bone fractures.
- ★ ☐ **Wire or "Ladder" Type Splints** — For splinting broken bones.
- ☐ Air Splints — For fractured bone immobilization.
- ★ ☐ **Sterile Tongue Blades** — To check for sore throat and to splint broken fingers.
- ☐ Cardboard Splints — For fractured bone immobilization.
- ☐ Magazines — For splinting fractured bones.
- ● Splints can also be fashioned from pillows, boards, ski poles, umbrellas, or rolled up newspapers. They can be secured with belts.
- ● Crutches can be fashioned from forked sticks if nothing better is available.
- ★ ☐ **Instant Chemical Disposable Hotpack** — Increases blood circulation, helps reduce pain.
- ★ ☐ **Instant Chemical Disposable Coldpack** — To reduce swelling, for burns, for relief of pain.
- ☐ Rubber Hot Water Bottle — For relief of pain.
- ☐ Plastic Ice Bag — To reduce swelling, for burns, for relief of pain.

- ★ **Sterile Bulb Aspirator, 2 or 3 Ounce Size**—To suck blood and other secretions from the back of the throat and from the nostrils; essential for emergency childbirth.
- **Laerdal-Type Pocket Mask**—As an aid to give mouth-to-mouth without actual contact to skin.
- **Hudson-Type Airways, Assorted Sizes**—To help keep the airway open.
- **Berman-Type Airways, Assorted Sizes**
- **Endotracheal Intubation Kit with Laryngascope and Blades**—For emergency airway management.
- **Resusci Bag, Adult and Child Sizes**—For airway ventilatory purposes.
- **Filter Masks, Dust or Surgical Type**—Reduces the spread of germs.
- ★ **Mouth-To-Mouth Instructions**—On a small card.
- ★ **Choking First Aid Instructions**—On a small card.
- ★ **CPR Instructions**—On small card.
- **Rubbing Alcohol (70%) Isopropyl**—For poison ivy, to sterilize, to cool the body (except infants), or to clean hands.
- **Sterile Water or Normal Saline Solution in Plastic Bottle**—For wound irrigation, cleansing, cooling burns.
- **Distilled Water in a Plastic Bottle**—One pint for wound cleansing, cooling burns.
- **Small Bar of Soap**—For cleaning wounds.
- ★ **Small Container of Sterile Liquid Soap**—For cleaning wounds, such as Phisoderm.
- **Tincture of Green Soap Pads**—For cleaning hands, wounds.
- ★ **Pair of Latex Sterile Gloves**—To prevent further contamination of wounds, reducing chances of infection.
- ★ **Oral Thermometer, Pencil Case**—To determine body temperature.
- ★ **Rectal Thermometer, Pencil Case**—To determine body temperature.
- ★ **Vaseline**—For lubrication of rectal thermometer, for chapped lips, etc.
- **K-Y Gel**—For lubrication of rectal thermometer.
- **Magill Intubation Forceps, Adult and Child Size**—To remove foreign objects or food lodged in the back of the throat.
- **Sharp Knife or Razor Blade**—For cutting.
- ★ **Safety Pins of Various Sizes**—To tie bandages.

- **Sterile Scalpel**
- **Seizure Bite Stick**—To help prevent convulsive patient from biting tongue.
- ★ **Paper Drinking Cups**—To give drinks and to cover eye injuries.
- ★ **One Ounce Plastic Measuring Cup**—For measuring out medicines.
- ★ **Syringe-Type Medication Dispenser**—(5ccs equals one teaspoon.)
- **Plastic Measuring Spoon**—For giving medications.
- **Medicine Eye Dropper**—To rinse eyes or to give medications.
- ★ **First Aid Manual, American Medical Association**—For first aid instructions.
- **Reader's Digest First Aid Manual**—For first aid instructions.
- ★ **Names, Phone Numbers, and Addresses** of physician, hospital, paramedics, police, fire department, poison control center, etc. Refer to Communications Section for additional phone numbers you may want to include.
- ★ **Critical Medical Histories Required by Family Members**
- ★ **Paper and Pencil**—To record medical information and to send messages.
- ★ **Small Flashlight or Re-useable Penlight with Extra Alkaline Batteries**—To examine throat and contractility of pupils of eyes and to offer medical assistance in dark situations.
- ★ **Emergency Blanket 84" x 56"**—To treat shock. Refer to Bedding section for a complete description.
- ★ **Matches, Waterproofed**—To sterilize needles, scissors, or dressings.
- ★ **Emesis Basin or "Airsick Bag"**—From commercial airlines or regular plastic bag and tie (for vomiting).
- ★ **Cutter Brand Snake Bite Kit**—For treatment of snake bites.
- **Spring Loaded Center Punch**—For breaking windows in auto extrication operations.
- ★ **Medic-Alert Tags, Bracelets or I.D.**—If applicable.
- **Emergency Medical Certification**
- ★ **Olive Oil and Vile**
- **Small Towel**—For drying.
- **Cotton Balls, Sterile**—For application of medications to skin. Do not use on open wounds.
- **Q-tip Cotton Applicators**—For application of skin medications.

☐ Extra Pair of Contac Lenses — If applicable.

☐ Contact Lens Solution

☐ Prescription Eyeglasses, Extra Pair — If applicable.

☐ Extra Hearing Aid Batteries — If applicable.

☐ Hearing Protectors, Foam Type — To reduce noise intake.

☐ Prosthetic Devices

☐ Star of Life Decals, 3" x 3" — To identify your first aid kit.

☐ Small Backpack — To store and transport the first aid and medication supplies listed.

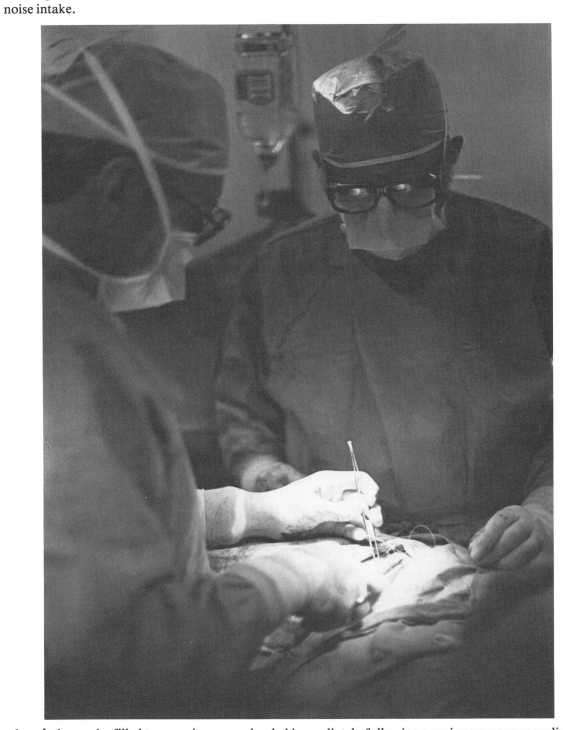

Since hospitals may be filled to capacity or overloaded immediately following a major emergency or disaster, it is wise for family members to gain a working knowledge of basic emergency first aid. *Photo — Utah Valley Hospital, Provo, Utah.*

MEDICATIONS

   Needed medications often become a rare commodity during and after many disasters and other emergencies. A needed medication will not only provide relief of physical discomfort and pain associated with injury or disease, but will, as a result, help reduce the level of an already elevated stress level from the disaster itself. **It is wise to work with and consult your physician and your local pharmacy in obtaining necessary medications for your kit.**

- Medicines for chronic illnesses usually require daily medications. Include an extra several days or weeks of these medications (Diabetes, heart condition, etc.).

- Be sure all medicine containers are adequately labeled and that directions for use are kept with each of them.

- Keep a record of expiration dates and replace your medications with a fresh supply when the times comes.

- **Use only those medications or procedures you are familiar with or are qualified to administer.**

   A star ★ by an item indicates that it is essential or strongly suggested.

★ ☐ **Adult Aspirin Tablets** (analgesic)

★ ☐ **Adult Tylenol, Acetaminophen** (analgesic)

★ ☐ **Strong Pain Medication** — Prescription, consult your physician.

★ ☐ **Baby Chewable Aspirins** (analgesic)

★ ☐ **Children's Tylenol, Acetiminophen** (analgesic)

★ ☐ **Infant Tempra Drops, Acetiminophen** (analgesic) — If applicable.

☐ Alka-Seltzer — Antacid, analgesic.

☐ Throat Lozenges — Such as Sucrets, anesthetic.

☐ Salt Water Gargle — For sore throat.

☐ Rolaids, Tums — Antacid.

☐ Mylanta or Di-Gel Liquid — For gas, acid indigestion.

☐ Milk of Magnesia — Laxative, antacid.

☐ Maalox or Riopan — For upset stomach.

★ ☐ **Lomotil Tablets** — Perscription, for diarrhea.

☐ Kaopectate — Relief of diarrhea.

☐ Paragoric Liquid — Prescription, to control diarrhea.

☐ Sulfasuxidine — Prescription, for dysentery.

☐ Epsom Salts — For a laxative in case of poisoning.

★ ☐ **Metamucil** — Bulk laxative for constipation.

☐ Fleet Enema — For severe constipation.

☐ Penicillin Tablets — Prescription, antibiotic, for bacterial infections.

☐ Amoxicillin Tablets — Prescription, antibiotic for bacterial infections.

☐ Ampicillin — Prescription, antibiotic for bacterial infections.

☐ Achromycin Capsules — Prescription, antibiotic for bacterial infections.

☐ Triaminic Syrup — For colds, allergies.

☐ Sudafed Tablets — Decongestant for colds and allergies.

★ ☐ **Actifed** — Antihistamine, decongestant.

☐ Drixoral — Antihistamine, decongestant.

★ ☐ **Neosynephrine Nasal Spray** — 0.25% for children, 0.5% for adults. For nasal congestion, sinusitis. Use Afrin nasal spray if pregnant, unless your physician advises otherwise.

★ ☐ **Robitussin-DM** — For cough control.

★ ☐ **Promethazine with Codeine** — For severe coughing, prescription.

☐ Cough Drops — Cough suppressor.

☐ Mentholatum or Vicks VapoRub — For colds.

☐ Hay Fever Pills — Antihistamine.

☐ Parapectolin — Prescription, long acting antihistamine for allergic reactions, stings, and other allergy problems.

★ ☐ **Benadryl** (Diphenhydramine) — For congestion, allergic reactions, itching or restlessness, prescription.

☐ Caladry Lotion — Relief of allergy caused skin problems.

- ★ ☐ **Calamine Lotion** — For treatment of poison ivy, poison sumac, poison oak, and to soothe minor bites and stings.
- ☐ Epinephrine Injection Kit — For treatment of anaphalactic shock, severe allergic reactions. Qualified individuals only may administer this medication.
- ☐ Inhaler, Broncho-Dilator — Opens up lung passages. For chronic illnesses, such as asthma.
- ★ ☐ **Syrup of Ipecac** — To induce vomiting in poison cases.
- ☐ Activated Charcoal — To bind or absorb poison.
- ★ ☐ **Insect Repellent** — Roll-on, spray, or wipe on.
  - Crushed ferns or wild onions can be rubbed on as an insect repellent in an emergency if nothing else is available.
- ★ ☐ **Campho-phenique** — For minor wounds and insect bites.
- ☐ Cornstarch Powder — To treat diaper rash, if applicable.
- ☐ Desiten Diaper Ointment — To treat diaper rash, if applicable.
- ☐ Tinactine, Selsun, or Desenex — Antifungal.
- ★ ☐ **Neosporin Ointment** — For skin infections, antibacterial ointment for minor wounds.
- ★ ☐ **Alcohol Preparation Pads** — Germacide, to clean or disinfect a wound.
- ★ ☐ **Betadine Preparation Pads** — Antiseptic, germacide, to clean or disinfect a wound.
- ☐ Betadine Solution or Scrub Solution in Plastic Containers — Antiseptic, germacide.
- ☐ Hydrogen Proxide — Antiseptic for minor cuts and abrasions. Helps dissolve blood in clothing, etc.
- ★ ☐ **Block-Out or Pre-Sun, Paba-Film, Pabonol** — For use as a sunscreen.
- ☐ Solarcaine — For sunburns.
- ☐ Chapstick — For chapped lips.
- ★ ☐ **Zinc Oxide** — For chapped lips and minor burns.
- ☐ Cortisone (Prednisone) — Prescription, bursitis, allergic reactions.
- ☐ Hydrocortisone Cream — For itching skin.
- ☐ Vaseline Intensive Care Lotion — For dry skin.
- ☐ Auralgan Ear Drops — Prescription, for ear infections.
- ☐ Cortisporin — Ear drops.
- ☐ Debrox Drops — For ear wax.

- ☐ Butyn or Pontocaine — Prescription, eye anesthetic.
- ☐ Spectrocin or Bacitracin, Cortisporin — Prescription, for eye infection.
- ★ ☐ **Vaso-Clear Eye Drops** — For eye irritations.
- ☐ Oil of Cloves — To place on cotton for toothache.
- ☐ Seconal — Prescription, for sleeplessness.
- ☐ Caffeine Tablets — Such as No-doz, to stay awake.
- ☐ Compazine — Prescription, for nausea or vomiting.
- ☐ Morning Sickness Pills — Prescription, consult your physician to obtain a safe drug.
- ★ ☐ **Table Salt** — To dilute with water to administer for delayed treatment of shock and burns and for treatment of heat cramps and fatigue and to make salt water to gargle with to treat a sore throat.
- ★ ☐ **Salt Tablets** — For treatment of heat emergencies and fatigue.
- ★ ☐ **Baking Soda** — In small container for third degree burns and shock.
- ★ ☐ **Sugar Cubes** — Individually wrapped in plastic or restaurant sugar packets, for insulin shock.
- ☐ Gantrisin — Prescription, for urinary tract infections.
- ☐ Insulin — For diabetics, regulates blood sugar level, prescription. Keep refrigerated as a last minute item to bring along.
- ★ ☐ **Other Prescription Medications Currently Taking, Such As Heart Tablets** — Check with your doctor to obtain an additional supply for your kit.
- ★ ☐ **Each individual in the family should be current on tetanus immunization** — Prevents lockjaw as a result of puncture wounds with metal objects.
- ☐ I.V. Injection Kit with Proper Solutions and Drugs
- ☐ Anti-Venum Serum Injection Kit — Prescription, for treatment of poisonous snake bites.
- ☐ Oxygen, Small Canister, and Mask — To treat shock and chronic lung diseases.

Surging flood waters from a broken dam raged through a 100-mile stretch of the Teton and Snake Rivers, bringing suffering and losses to nearly 5,000 families. Several thousand homes and businesses were destroyed or damaged. Residents had only about 20 minutes warning of the fast approaching wall of water.

Near Rexburg, Idaho, 1976. *American Red Cross photo by Phil Gibson.*

TOILETRIES

In a disaster or emergency, some of the everyday toiletry items we so often take for granted suddenly become luxury items. Having these items will also do a great deal to "normalize" an emergency situation, reducing levels of stress.

The following items in this and the sanitation section should be placed in an approximately five-gallon plastic polyethylene bucket with a tight fitting lid and a carrying handle. The diameter of the container should be approximately twelve inches. The container can double as a makeshift toilet.

Purchase small trial or sample size products in plastic containers if possible.

Starred ★ items are essential or strongly suggested.

★ ☐ **Five-Gallon Plastic Container with Handle and Tight Lid** — Ask your local grocer where these can be obtained in your area.

★ ☐ **Two Extra Lids to Above Container** — Cut out the center and pad the rims for added comfort as an improvised adult and children's toilet seat.

★ ☐ **Toilet Paper** — Waterproofed.

★ ☐ **Small Bar of Soap**

★ ☐ **Bar Soap Holder** — Plastic.

★ ☐ **One-Gallon (approx.) Plastic Wash Basin** — Fits into five-gallon main container.

★ ☐ **Shampoo, Small Plastic Container** — There are shampoos on the market like those used in hospitals that do not need to be rinsed from the hair.

☐ Hair Rinse and Conditioner — Small container.

☐ Baby Lotion

★ ☐ **Toothpaste or Tooth Powder** — Baking soda or salt can also be used.

★ ☐ **Toothbrushes**

☐ Toothpicks

☐ Dental Floss

☐ Fingernail and Toenail Clippers

★ ☐ **Insect Repellent** — Stick, towelettes, or spray.

☐ Deodorant Stick or Anti-perspirant

☐ Plastic Razor

☐ Razor with Blades

★ ☐ **Desitin Diaper Ointment** — If applicable.

☐ Cornstarch Powder

☐ Baby Powder

★ ☐ **Chapstick**

☐ Vaseline

★ ☐ **Kleenex Facial Tissue** — Small package.

★ ☐ **Small Metal or Glass Mirror with Cover**

★ ☐ **Comb**

☐ Hairbrush-Small

★ ☐ **Small Bath Towel**

★ ☐ **Washcloth**

☐ OB Moistened Towelettes

★ ☐ **Regular Moistened Towelettes or Wipes** — For cleaning hands, face, or for a messy diaper problem. Each individually wrapped.

★ ☐ **Feminine Hygiene Needs**

☐ Special Nursing Needs — Pads, etc.

☐ Mouthwash

☐ Extra Pair of Prescription Glasses

☐ Extra Pair of Contact Lenses

☐ Contact Lens Solution

☐ Make-up — Small container.

☐ Small Hair Curlers/Pins

★ ☐ **Liquid All Purpose Body Soap** — Small container.

☐ Shaving Cream or Lotion

☐ Hair Cream

☐ Small Shoehorn

☐ Hand Lotion

☐ Breath Mints — Such as Tic-Tacs or spray-type.

☐ Q-Tip Applicators

☐ Cotton Balls

☐ Cushioned Insoles for Shoes

☐ Foot Powder

SANITATION

Sanitation can be a monumental problem during an emergency if advanced preparations have not been made. Toilet facilities will not function if water has been cut off, as is usually the case in a disaster. Therefore, it is very wise to plan for and to prepare an alternate (and portable) method of sanitation.

- **The five-gallon container discussed above in the Toiletries Section will function in an excellent manner for a makeshift toilet.** Several of the items listed below will serve to augment your sanitation system in preventing the spread of disease and odors. Remember that the lid must be kept tightly on the container to prevent the spread of germs.

Starred ★ items are essential or strongly suggested.

★ ☐ **Four-Gallon Capacity White Wastepaper Basket Plastic Bags and Ties**—2 packages of 24 each for use in the makeshift toilet.

★ ☐ **Large Grocery Bags** (6)—For use in conjunction with disposal of solid wastes.

★ ☐ **Small Can of Lysol Disinfectant**—To help retard the spread of germs.

☐ Small Container of Liquid Chlorine Bleach

★ ☐ **Folding Camp Shovel with Serrated Cutting Edge**—For digging latrines and disposing of wastes.

★ ☐ **Deodorizer Tablets**—To reduce odors.

★ ☐ **Large Trash Bag and Tie**—32-gallon garbage liner.

☐ Collapsible Camping Toilet—Uses plastic bags.

☐ Small Portable Potty

☐ Plastic Bedpan

☐ Ammonia—As an aid in disinfecting.

★ ☐ **Laundry Detergent**—Small vendor box.

☐ Bleach—Small vendor box.

☐ Clothes Pins—To hang up wet clothing.

★ ☐ **Cotton Dish Towel**

★ ☐ **Paper Towels**

★ ☐ **Regular Sponge**

★ ☐ **3M-Type Scrubbing Sponge or Scouring Pad**

☐ Pocket Tube Soap—For face, hands, and dishes.

- If in a wilderness area, select a suitable spot at least fifty feet from any open water. Dig a hole no more than six to eight inches deep to stay in the "biological disposer" layer of soil. Save the sod or dirt. After use, fill the hole with soil and tramp the sod back in place.

- When man is forced to adjust quickly from a civilized environment, with all its comforts, to an existence much like that of a caveman, body systems are upset, and one often develops gastro-intestinal problems which compound the problems of sanitation.

Small children's fears are often magnified in a disaster. Careful advance preparation can help reduce a child's emotional trauma and provide a degree of comfort and assurance during an emergency. *Photo courtesy American Red Cross.*

INFANT & SMALL CHILDREN NEEDS

In a major emergency, being without small children's needs is a disaster in itself. On the other hand, having prepared in advance by gathering up a few needed items will make a world of difference. The crisis will, as a result, be much more bearable for both the children and the parents.

A star ★ by an item indicates that it is essential or strongly suggested.

- ☐ Infant Formula – Liquid concentrate in cans.
- ☐ Infant Formula – Powdered, in small packets.
- ☐ Substitute Formula – If allergies are present.
- ☐ Strained Baby Foods – Such as Gerber.
- ☐ Baby Cereal – Small boxes or packets.
- ☐ Sugared Cereals – Small boxes or packets.
- ☐ Strained Baby Fruit Juices – Such as Gerber.
- ☐ Animal Crackers or "Penny Candy" – Refer to Food Section.
- ☐ Plastic Baby Bottles with Lids and Nipples
- ☐ Bottle/Nipple Scrub Brushes
- ☐ Disposable Diapers
- ☐ Curity Cloth Diapers
- ☐ Desiten Diaper Ointment – For diaper rash.
- ☐ Cornstarch – For diaper rash.
- ☐ Baby Lotion or Cream
- ☐ Baby Powder
- ☐ Moist Towelettes – Such as "Wet Ones" or "Handy Wipes."
- ☐ Plastic Bibs – Available for free at fast food restaurants.
- ★ ☐ **Liquid Baby Vitamins or Chewable Children's Vitamins**
- ★ ☐ **Baby Chewable Flavored Aspirin**
- ★ ☐ **Liquid Tylenol for Children (Acetaminophen) or Tempra Drops for Infants**
- ★ ☐ **Pacifier** – If applicable.
- ★ ☐ **Metal Whistle** – For small children, if separated. Carries further than voice.
- ☐ Plastic or Rubber Pants – Two pair.
- ☐ Diaper Safety Pins
- ☐ Small Inflatable Air Mattress

- ☐ Small Rubberized Bedsheet
- ☐ Cotton or Muslin Bedsheet
- ☐ Q-Tip Applicators
- ☐ Special Nursing Needs – Pads, etc.
- ☐ Baby Oil
- ★ ☐ **Baby Soap** – Or other mild soap, preferably liquid soap in a small, plastic container.
- ☐ Baby Shampoo
- ☐ Small Scissors or Clippers for Fingernails and Toenails
- ☐ Cotton Balls
- ☐ Baby Brush or Comb
- ☐ Tongs – For baby bottles.
- ☐ Funnel – Small plastic.
- ☐ Container – To heat up baby bottles.
- ★ ☐ **Knit Mittens**
- ☐ Baby Washcloths
- ☐ Large Baby Bath Towel
- ★ ☐ **Large Warm Baby Blanket, Shawl, or Wrapper**
- ★ ☐ **Warm Socks**
- ☐ Warm Booties – If not walking.
- ★ ☐ **Walking Shoes**
- ☐ Cotton Blankets
- ★ ☐ **Wool Blankets**
- ★ ☐ **Pediatric Oral/Rectal Thermometer**
- ★ ☐ **Several Shirts with Sleeves**
- ★ ☐ **Undershirts**
- ☐ "Sleepers" or Nightgowns
- ★ ☐ **Sweaters, Opening in Front (Cardigans)**
- ★ ☐ **Coat or Heavy Weight Waterproof Jacket with Hood**

★ ☐ **Knit Ski-Type Stocking Hat**

☐ Blanket Sleeper with Feet

☐ Bunting Bag — For small babies.

☐ Pair of Coveralls or Long Pants

★ ☐ **Benadryl** — Prescription, for allergic reactions, congestion, itching, and restlessness.

★ ☐ **Rattle, Small Toys, Stuffed Animals** — Refer to Recreation Section for additional ideas.

● Maternity product sample packs can be obtained at your local hospital maternity ward for free or for a nominal charge. They contain many trial, sample size baby products which would be excellent for your kit.

A rarity in times past, active volcanoes are today surprisingly frequent. Volcanoes have the potential for massive destruction, especially in densely populated areas.

Mt. Saint Helens, Washington, 1980. *Photo courtesy Federal Emergency Management Agency.*

DOCUMENTS

Include in your kit copies of important, valuable, irreplaceable or cherished records. You may also want to leave copies of important papers in a sealed packet put in a safety deposit box or left with a friend or relative living in a different location, preferably in another city or town. Be sure to place the documents in a waterproof container. Color photocopying is now available for duplicating color photos, certificates, or color documents.

A star ★ by an item indicates that it is essential or strongly suggested.

★ ☐ **Photo Inventory of Home, Premises, Garage, Other Real Estate Holdings, and Place of Business** — Refer to section on Home Security and Protection for a complete explanation.

★ ☐ **Insurance Documents, I.D. Cards and Phone Numbers**

★ ☐ **Stocks, Bonds, and Certificates**

☐ Achievement Certificates

☐ High School and College Degrees

☐ Birth Certificates

★ ☐ **Social Security Cards/Numbers**

☐ Important or Cherished Recipes

★ ☐ **All Legal Papers**

★ ☐ **Deeds**

★ ☐ **Wills**

★ ☐ **Savings Account Number and Bank Location**

☐ Passbook Duplicate and Number

★ ☐ **Checking Account Number and Bank Location**

★ ☐ **Savings Certificate Numbers and Bank Location**

☐ Driver's License

★ ☐ **Gas Card Numbers and Names of Companies**

★ ☐ **Charge Card Numbers and Names of Companies**

★ ☐ **Check Guarantee Card Number and Location**

★ ☐ **Copies of Important Contracts**

★ ☐ **Copy of Investment Portfolio**

★ ☐ **Immunization Records**

☐ Passports

☐ Visas

☐ Journals

☐ Genealogy

☐ "Four Generation" Sheets

☐ Personal History

☐ Family History

☐ Pedigree Charts

☐ Cherished Photos, Slides, Negatives, or Films and Videos

☐ Patriarchal Blessings

☐ Line of Priesthood Authority

☐ Memory Books

☐ Books of Remembrance

☐ Original Manuscripts

☐ Biographies

MONEY

An instant supply of emergency cash during or after a disaster could be "priceless." Returning home after evacuating may be, at the least, traumatic. Your home may have been swept away by raging torrents, covered by volcanic ash, destroyed by a violent tornado, knocked off its foundation by a powerful earthquake, crushed by a wall of mud, or gutted by a devastating fire. In other words, your house may be uninhabitable. This would force you and your family to fend for yourselves until other provisions are made. Having a ready supply of cash would help put you back on your feet and would permit you to buy services you may be in desperate need of. In reference to money, we all would do well to do as the TV ad says, which is: "Don't leave home without it."

A star ★ by an item indicates that it is essential or strongly suggested.

★ ☐ **Cash, $100 to $200 in One Dollar Bills** — Place these in a waterproof Zip-loc-type plastic bag.

★ ☐ **Pocket Change**

    ☐ Quarters — One roll
    ☐ Dimes — One roll
    ☐ Nickels — One roll
    ☐ Pennies — One Roll

☐ Silver — Several one-ounce ingots.

☐ Traveler's Checks

☐ Money Orders

☐ Checkbook and Register

★ ☐ **Check Protection or Guarantee Card** — Duplicate.

★ ☐ **Visa or MasterCard** — Duplicate.

★ ☐ **Gasoline Charge Cards** — Duplicates.

★ ☐ **Other Charge Cards, Phone, Etc.** — Duplicates.

☐ Gold Jewelry — Last minute item.

★ ☐ **Postage Stamps** — Various amounts.

☐ Small Pocket Calculator

☐ Spare House Keys

☐ Spare Car Keys

The typical hurricane brings six to twelve inches of rainfall to the area it crosses, usually in only a few hours. Resulting floods produce great damage and loss of life. Stay indoors during a hurricane. Travel is extremely dangerous when wind and tides are whipping through your area.

Hurricane Frederic, Mobile, Alabama, 1979. *Photo courtesy National Oceanic and Atmospheric Administration.*

RECREATION

Good morale is one of the single greatest factors in successfully coping with a major evacuation emergency or disaster. Having a few diversion items on hand will help to fortify a person's social, emotional and spiritual strength. Carefully selected diversion items will be your defense against despair and stress, brightening the mood and adding a sense of calmness and security. Recreational items will also help to occupy the long periods of time in which there may be very little to do.

A star ★ by an item indicates that it is essential or strongly suggested.

★ ☐ **Scriptures**
☐ Hymn Book
☐ Paperback Books
☐ Reader's Digest Magazines
★ ☐ **Other Magazines**
☐ Songbook
☐ Sheet Music
☐ Small Musical Instrument such as a Harmonica
★ ☐ **Small Journal or Notebook**
★ ☐ **Paper**
★ ☐ **Pencils**
★ ☐ **Pens**
☐ Needlework
☐ Checkers—Small version
☐ Chess—Small version
☐ Other Small, Flat Games
☐ Small Card Games, such as UNO
☐ FM/AM Radio Cassette—Such as the "Walkman" type.
☐ Pre-recorded Favorite Music or Talks
☐ Small Pocket Type TV—Put on your last minute items list. Very small televisions are on the market, such as the wrist-watch type or the Casio brand TV which measures only one inch by 3½ inches by 5 inches, weighing only 12 ounces. Be sure to include an extra battery.
☐ Small Pocket Camera
☐ Film
☐ Golf Club and Ball
☐ Softball
☐ Quiet Books
☐ Coloring Books
☐ Small Package of Crayons

☐ Colored Pencils
☐ Small Pencil Sharpener
☐ Small Play Toys
☐ Small Rubber Ball for Children
☐ Matchbox Cars
★ ☐ **Favorite "Teddy Bear" or Security Blanket**— Your little ones will appreciate your thoughtfulness by including such items. Put the items on your "last minute" list. These can really be a "lifesaver" in a stressful emergency.
☐ Dominos
☐ Paper Paste or Glue
☐ Small Pair of Paper Scissors
☐ Colored Construction Paper
☐ Watercolor Paint Set
☐ Word Games
☐ Picture Games
☐ Simple Math and Spelling Games
☐ Flashcards
☐ Mini-Pens
☐ Fun Pad/Children's Workbook
☐ Flannelboard Stories
☐ Game Books
☐ Car Travel Games
☐ Puzzles
☐ "Jacks"
☐ Small Jump Rope
☐ "Rubik's" Cube
☐ Small Squirt Gun
☐ Frisbee—Large or miniature.
☐ Small Yo-Yo or Top
☐ Baby Rattle
☐ Small Homemade Puppets

If you are in a moving car during an earthquake, stop as quickly as safety permits, but stay in your car. A car may jiggle fearsomely on its springs, but it is a good place to stay until the shaking stops. When you drive on, watch for hazards created by the earthquake, such as fallen objects, downed electrical wires, or broken or undermined roadways.

Collapsed overpass connecting Foothill Boulevard and Golden State Freeway. San Fernando Earthquake, Los Angeles County, California, 1971. *Photo courtesy U.S. Geological Survey.*

TRANSPORTATION

When we think about transportation for an emergency evacuation, we look out the window at our car or camper, and we don't give it a second thought. However, what if a member of the family was using the car when the need to evacuate came? What if the car was being repaired or perhaps was out of gas? Or, what if the road conditions were such that it would not be feasible or wise or even possible to use them to leave the area? Unforeseen circumstances such as these are reason enough to consider and to have ready one or two alternate forms of transportation. **Several options are listed below.**

Starred ★ items are essential or strongly suggested.

★ ☐ **Automobile — Keep in good repair with gas tank at least one-half full at all times and with plenty of antifreeze/summer coolant in the radiator.**

☐ Camper

☐ Motorcycle

☐ Bicycle

☐ Small Home-made Handcart

☐ Utility Trailer

☐ Walk Out on Foot

☐ If you drive a small automobile, a car-top luggage rack is a good idea to have.

☐ Wheelbarrow

☐ Shopping Carts

☐ Grocery Totes — The kind used to pull a bag or two of groceries home with you.

☐ Suitcase Carriers — The kind seen at airports with luggage on them.

☐ Large Baby Stroller

☐ A Large Wagon (Children's) — Such as the "radio-flyer" type.

☐ Push Carts or Hand Trucks — The kind used in grocery stores to move heavy boxes of food items from one location to another.

☐ An Inflatable Raft — If a very serious flooding situation exists in your area.

- Keep in mind the transportation needs of the bed- or wheelchair-ridden person.
- Don't drive unless necessary and drive with caution. Watch for hazards to yourself and others and report them to local authorities.
- Travel with care. If your local government is arranging transportation for you, precautions will be taken for your safety. But if you are walking or driving your own car to another location, remember the following:

- Make sure you have enough gasoline in your your car.
- Watch for washed out or undermined roadways, earth slides, broken sewer or water mains, loose or downed electrical wires, and and fallen objects.
- Watch out for areas where rivers and streams may flood suddenly.
- Don't try to cross a stream or pool of water unless you are certain that the water will not be over your knees or above the middle of your car's wheels, all the way across. Sometimes the water will hide a bridge or a part of the road that has been washed out. If you decide that it is safe to drive across it, put your car in low gear and drive very slowly to avoid splashing water into your engine and causing it to stop. Also, remember that your brakes may not work well after the wheels of your car have been in deep water. Try them out a few times when you reach the other side.
- Drive carefully along debris-filled streets. Roads may be undermined and may collapse under the weight of a car.
- During winter storms, travel only if necessary. Avoid all unnecessary trips. If you must travel, use public transportation if possible. However, if you are forced to use your automobile for a trip of any distance, take the following precautions:

  - Make sure your car is in good condition, properly serviced, and equipped with chains or snow tires.
  - Take another person with you if possible.
  - Make sure someone knows where you are going, your approximate schedule, and your estimated time of arrival.
  - Travel by daylight and use major highways if you can.

—Keep calm if you get in trouble or if your car breaks down. Flash your directional lights, raise the hood of your car, or hang a cloth from the radio aerial or car window. Wherever you are, if there is no house or other source of help in sight, do not leave your car to search for assistance; you may become confused and get lost.

—Have emergency "winter storm supplies" in the car, such as a container of sand, shovel, windshield scraper, tow chains or rope, and a flashlight. It is also good to have with you heavy gloves or mittens, overshoes, extra woolen socks, and winter headgear to cover your head and face. (Refer to sections on clothing and car equipment for a complete checklist.)

- **Avoid overexertion in winter storms.**

- *Leave early* enough so you won't be stranded by flooded roads, fallen wires or trees, or lots of cars.

- Heed traveler's warnings. Cold temperature and frequent storms require caution in planning, preparation, and travel. Winter storms should always be considered potentially dangerous to life and travel.

- During fall and winter daylight is short and temperatures may change suddenly. Rain quickly becomes snow.

- **Follow the routes recommended by authorities.**

- Stay away from disaster areas.

- **Listen to your radio** for information and instructions regarding the emergency.

- **Wear your car safety seat belts.**

- If you are below the highest level of potential flooding, select a high-ground area to which you can move if flooding is imminent.

- Stay out of flooded areas; the water may still be rising, and the current is unusually swift.

Residents in this and other homes narrowly escaped injury when giant boulders cascaded down nearby mountains, onto the small town of Challis (near Boise), Idaho, during a massive earthquake measuring 6.9 on the Richtor Scale. Two small children were killed while walking to school during the earthquake, which was felt in eight Western states and Canada.

Idaho Earthquake, November 1983. *Deseret News Photo by O. Wallace Kasteler.*

REPAIR KIT

The objective of your repair kit should be to have several different "raw" materials to make emergency repairs with. **Try to include only a very small quantity of each of the items** so you will be able to include more items and so that the weight of the repair kit will be minimal.

A starred ★ item indicates that it is essential or strongly suggested.

★ ☐ **Heavy Wire (steel)** — All purpose type, such as baling wire. Can be used to secure a splint or for many other uses.

★ ☐ **Light Wire (steel)** — All purpose type. Can even be used to substitute for a broken shoelace or for other uses.

★ ☐ **Duct Tape** (small roll) — Multiple purposes.

★ ☐ **Black Electrical Tape**

★ ☐ **Razor Blades**

★ ☐ **Assorted Safety Pins**

★ ☐ **Sewing Kit** (pocket size) — Needles, pins, seam ripper, thread, thimble, buttons, small scissors, paper tape measure.

★ ☐ **Shoelaces** — Various sizes.

★ ☐ **Boot Laces** — Various sizes.

★ ☐ **Nylon Rope** (50 feet) — Makeshift clothesline, construction of shelter, many repair uses.

★ ☐ **Grommets** — Refers to Shelter section for description and use.

★ ☐ **Rubber Patch Kit and Adhesive** — Rubber cement.

★ ☐ **Small Cutting Scissors** — Sharp.

★ ☐ **Small Can of WD-40 Silicone Lubricant**

★ ☐ **Small Piece of Thin Foam Rubber**

★ ☐ **Extra Fish Line** — Heavy weight.

☐ Dental Floss — Many varied uses in repair work.

★ ☐ **Krazy Glue or Permabond**

★ ☐ **Assorted Screws**

★ ☐ **Assorted Nails**

☐ Screw Hooks

☐ Screw Eyes

☐ Snap Hooks

☐ Thumbtacks

☐ Clasp Multi Pupose Knife

☐ Clothes Pins

☐ Worm or Hose Clamps — Assorted sizes.

☐ Small Magnet

☐ Paper Clips

☐ Plastic Straw

☐ Bobby Pins

☐ Straight Pins

☐ Nuts, Bolts, Washers

☐ Cellophane Tape

☐ Masking Tape

☐ Strapping Tape — Very strong.

☐ Assorted Compact Screwdriver Set

☐ Small Crescent Wrench

☐ Small File

☐ Hack Saw Blade

☐ Box Knife

☐ Welding Lead

☐ Heavy String

☐ Sandpaper — Fine and course.

☐ Assorted Rubber Bands

☐ Extra Piece of Nylon for Patches

☐ Rawhide Lacing

☐ Length of One-Inch Wide Elastic

☐ Small Stapler with Staples

☐ Wax Stick — Repairs leaks in seams of tents.

☐ Tent Repair Kit

☐ Nylon Repair Tape — For repair of nylon fabrics.

☐ Heavy Duty Aluminum Foil — Can be used as an emergency insole or to keep tinder dry, or as a windbreak for a small fire. Many more uses.

☐ Length of Rubber Surgical Tubing — For construction of sling shot or for use in the water "solar" still.

☐ Bungee or Shock Cords — For typing or hanging purposes.

☐ Velcro

Major streets in downtown Salt Lake City were turned into virtual rivers in a unique plan to divert damaging flood waters away from homes and businesses. The "river" eventually channeled into The Great Salt Lake, some ten miles away. *Salt Lake City, Utah, 1983.*

TOOLS

Adequate tools will be needed to obtain food, improve shelter, afford protection, and to make emergency repairs on your car.

A star ★ by an item indicates that it is essential or strongly suggested. **Starred tool items should be kept in your kit or easily accessible in your car.**

★ ☐ **Small Hand Ax or Hatchet and Case** — For cutting, chopping, driving tent stakes. Available at sporting goods stores.

☐ Ax

☐ Hammer

★ ☐ **Folding Camp Shovel with Serrated Cutting Edge** — For cutting firewood, ditching tents, digging latrines, and for building a snow cave or digging your car out of the snow. Available at sporting goods stores.

☐ Lightweight Garden Trowel — A less efficient form of a shovel, however, smaller.

★ ☐ **Pocket Knife** — Such as Boy Scout or Swiss Army type for cutting and use with flint. Available at sporting goods stores or Boy Scout retail outlets.

★ ☐ **Hunting Knife and Case** — Available at sporting goods stores.

★ ☐ **Small Bow Saw, Folding Type** — Available at sporting goods stores.

☐ Small Hacksaw with Extra Blades

★ ☐ **Pocket Hiker's Ring Saw** — Carry in pack. Available at Army surplus stores.

★ ☐ **Pliers with Fine Cutting Edge** — Insulated. Available at hardware stores.

★ ☐ **Adjustable, Insulated Pliers**

☐ Needle Nose Pliers — Insulated.

☐ Ratchet Set

★ ☐ **Large Screwdriver** (standard head) — Insulated.

★ ☐ **Large Screwdriver** (Phillip's head) — Insulated.

★ ☐ **Assorted Compact Screwdriver Set** — Available at K-Mart.

☐ Small Tape Measure

☐ Crowbar

☐ Length of Strong Rope

★ ☐ **Adjustable Insulated Crescent Wrench** — For turning off gas and water and for other emergency uses, such as car repairs. Available at hardware stores.

☐ Small File

☐ Ice Awl

☐ Snow Knife

☐ Pick

☐ Honing Kit, Stone and Oil — For sharpening knife.

• Every car hose converts to a siphon for getting at gasoline.

• The flat, round top of the air cleaner of your car be used for digging trenches or throwing up earthen wind screens.

☐ .22 Caliber Rimfire Semi-Automatic or Bolt Action Repeating Rifle — For hunting wild game.

☐ 200 Rounds of .22 Caliber Long Rifle Hollow Point Ammunition

CAR EQUIPMENT

Having a blowout on the freeway in the middle of the night, running out of gas, over-heating in the hot desert, or sliding off the road during a blizzard in the dead of winter—all of these are common, daily occurrences for lots of people everywhere. Having one of these events happen to your during a "normal" day is bad enough in itself, let alone during an emergency evacuation. It helps to be prepared with a few basic items for such dubious occasions.

Starred ★ items are essential or strongly suggested and should be kept in the trunk of your car at all times, especially during winter and on long trips.

★ ☐ **"Rescue Emergency Fuel"**—Non-explosive, safe to store in your trunk, takes you two to seven miles to a gas station. Have a minimum of two or three bottles. Available at auto parts stores.

☐ Plastic Funnel—For pouring fluids such as oil.

★ ☐ **Oil (2 Cans)**

☐ Oil Spout

☐ Oil Filter

★ ☐ **Power Steering Fluid**

☐ **Transmission Fluid**—Available at auto parts stores.

★ ☐ **Brake Fluid**—Available at auto parts stores.

☐ Windshield Washer Fluid

★ ☐ **Battery Booster Cables**—Available at auto parts stores.

☐ Extra Battery Cable

☐ Battery Cable Cleaner—Commercial type.

★ ☐ **Baking Soda and Old Toothbrush**—To clean off battery corrosion.

★ ☐ **Fan Belt**

★ ☐ **Spare Belts for Every Belt in the Engine**—Check with your car dealer or your mechanic.

★ ☐ **Extra Radiator and Heater Hoses**—With appropriate clamps.

★ ☐ **Worm or Hose Clamps**—Various sizes. Available at auto parts stores.

☐ Spare Water Pump

☐ Small Bar of Soap—An aid in putting on hoses.

★ ☐ **Duct Tape** (small roll)—Available at hardware stores. Helps to temporarily repair car hoses.

★ ☐ **Can of Liquid Sealer for Patching Minor Radiator Leaks**—Such as "Stop Leak." Available at auto parts stores.

★ ☐ **Lug Wrench**—For changing tires.

★ ☐ **Heavy Duty Jack**—Available at auto parts stores.

★ ☐ **Instructions for Changing Flat Tires**—Practice changing a tire if you've never done so.

★ ☐ **Spare Tire and Rim**—In good condition with correct air pressure.

☐ Tire Pressure Gauge

★ ☐ **Can of Tire Sealant Inflator**

☐ Flourescent Orange or Red Emergency Vinyl Vest—For high visibility while changing flat tire, etc.

☐ Umbrella

★ ☐ **Good Ice Scraper and Brush**—Available at auto parts stores.

★ ☐ **Small Bag of Sand or Gravel**—As a traction aid for removing your car from an icy rut.

☐ Gunny Sacks—For traction purposes.

★ ☐ **Foot Long Wood Planks** (2 pairs)—As a traction aid in getting your car out of mud or snow.

☐ Tire Pump

☐ Strong, Heavy-Duty Rope or Cable—For towing needs.

☐ Portable Winch

☐ Tow Chains—To pull car out of snow embankment or other towing needs.

☐ Aluminum Foil—For vapor lock.

☐ Carburetor Cleaning Spray

★ ☐ **Tool Kit**—For emergency auto repairs. Refer to Tools section of this book.

☐ Owner's Manual

★ ☐ **First Aid Kit**—Refer to First Aid section of this book.

★ ☐ **Mace or Riot Spray**—Stranded motorists are often the target of criminal activity.

☐ WD-40 Silicone Lubricant

☐ An **empty, clean** gas carrying can with pouring spout. CAUTION: Clean gas can after each use. Gas vapors may explode.

★ ☐ **Small Shovel**—Folding type with serrated cutting edge for digging out of snow. See Tools section of this book.

☐ Tire Chains (2 pairs)—For icy road conditions.

★ ☐ **Shell Answer Books** (set of 32)—Free from Shell Service Stations. Contains excellent car emergency repair information. Also available free by writing: Shell Answer Books, P.O. Box 61609, Houston, Texas 77208.

★ ☐ **$10.00 in Cash**—For emergency gas purchases.

★ ☐ **Dimes and Quarters**—For emergency phone calls.

★ ☐ **ABC Type Fire Extinguisher** (small canister)—Available at home centers and auto parts stores.

★ ☐ **Phone Numbers for Emergency Road Service and Local Law Enforcement Agency**—Such as the highway patrol.

★ ☐ **Baking Soda**—To put out fires.

☐ Distress Flag

☐ Multi-colored Balloons for Distress Signal

★ ☐ **Emergency Road Distress Flares**—Available at auto parts stores.

☐ Emergency Reflectors

★ ☐ **Emergency, Easy-to-Understand Car Repair Handbook**—For minor car repairs. Check with your local bookstore or write for your free Shell Answer Books, which contain emergency car repair information.

☐ Emergency Fuse Kit

★ ☐ **Extra Pair of Windshield Wipers**

☐ Air Filter

☐ Small Tin Can

☐ Small Candles or Canned Heat—To melt snow in a tin can for drinking water if snowbound.

☐ Winter Snow Tires with Studs—Have available and ready to put on your car.

★ ☐ **Clean Rags**—To work on the car with and to clean headlights or taillights.

☐ Roll of Paper Towels

☐ Old Blanket or Large Towel—To kneel or lay on while working under the car.

★ ☐ **Flashlight with Extra Alkaline Batteries**—For working on the car at night.

★ ☐ **Plastic Siphon Pump**—For getting at your's or another car's gasoline for emergency use.

☐ Gas Cap with Lock and Key

☐ "Frost Shield"—For windshield frost protection.

☐ Replacement Auto Bulbs—Such as brakelights, etc.

☐ Spark Plugs and Wrench

☐ Anti-Freeze/Summer Coolant—One gallon.

★ ☐ **Water (1 gallon)**—For low radiator or battery fluid levels.

☐ Extra Heater Thermostat

☐ Engine Starting Fluid

☐ Blank Accident Report Form

★ ☐ **Auto Insurance Card**

★ ☐ **Driver's License**

★ ☐ **All Purpose Strong Wire**—Such as baling wire to lash down a sprung trunk, etc.

☐ Plastic Waterbag

☐ *How to Save Big Bucks on Car Repairs*—By Robert Demotte, (801) 226-3241, c/o Roma Publishing, Code (E), P.O. Box 1717, Provo, Utah 84603. Contains excellent information on car repairs and how to not get "ripped off."

● **Your car should always be kept in good repair, and your gas tank should always be kept at least one-half full at all times, even though it requires frequent gas stops. In the winter, if you get stuck in the snow, you'll need the gas to help you run the heater at frequent intervals to stay warm.**

● **Some extra warm clothing and non-perishable foods are good to store in your trunk for long winter trips.**

Home fires can be devastating in a matter of minutes. Properly installed smoke detectors, class ABC fire extinguishers, and a well-rehearsed family fire escape plan are a must for every home.

Salt Lake City Fire Department photo by Kenneth Dailey.

HOME SECURITY & PROTECTION

Safeguarding one's home before, during, and after an emergency is an integral part of emergency preparedness. Following preventive measures may help to prevent or limit property damage or vandalism to not only one's home, but also to priceless possessions and treasures.

Starred ★ items are essential or strongly suggested.

★ ☐ **Shut Off Water** — Open faucets slightly.

☐ Turn Down Water Heaters or Drain Them

☐ Turn Down Heat Thermostats

☐ Shut Off Air Conditioner

★ ☐ **Shut Off Gas** — Main valve.

☐ Shut Off Gas Appliances

★ ☐ **Shut Off Electricity** — Main breaker.

☐ Disconnect All Electrical Appliances Except Food Storage.

☐ Prepare Garbage for Normal Pickup — Minimizes rodents and insects.

☐ Close and lock all doors inside and out and all windows. Open some windows if the emergency is a tornado.

☐ Put tape across windows and mirrors to reduce flying glass damage. You may want to install storm shutters to protect windows.

☐ Keep sandbags, plywood, plastic sheeting, and lumber handy for emergency waterproofing. But if flooding is imminent, *do not* stack sandbags around the outside walls of your house to keep flood waters out of your basement. In most cases it is better to permit the flood waters to flow freely into the basement. This will equalize the water pressure on the outside of the basement walls and floors and thus avoid structural damage to the foundation and the house.

☐ Keep valuable documents in safe deposit box or a sturdy fireproof, waterproof metal box or take them with you in a proper container. Refer to Documents section of this book. NOTE: A refrigerator is waterproof and fireproof, if you want to put documents in it at the last minute before leaving.

☐ Have Class ABC fire extinguishers in various locations in your home, garage, and business.

☐ If evacuation threat is flooding, move furniture and valuables to upper levels.

★ ☐ **Have properly installed smoke detectors in various locations of your home** (both the ionization and photoelectric type). It's not the fire but rather the smoke which kills. Rarely does an individual detect the smoke in time while sleeping.

☐ Have a portable fire escape ladder for your home or apartment if there are multiple floors.

☐ Board up windows if necessary. Danger to small windows is mainly from wind-driven debris. Larger windows may be broken by wind pressure.

☐ Cover jewelry, cameras, coin collections, etc., with a special "floater" insurance.

☐ Obtain special types of weather insurance you may need in your area.

☐ Review your homeowner's policy for burglary protection.

☐ Flood losses are not covered under normal homeowners' insurance policies, but flood insurance is available in participating communities through the federally-sponsored National Flood Insurance program. Contact your local insurance broker or agent for more information.

☐ Have or install deadbolt locks on all exterior doors.

☐ Have a home security alarm system installed.

☐ Keep a list of credit cards, etc., at home in a safe place.

☐ Keep spare house and car keys in a magnetic container hidden beneath your car. Never hide a spare house key anywhere else, except perhaps in your wallet.

☐ Park your other cars you're not evacuating with in your garage. Roll up the car windows and lock the car doors and be sure to close and lock the garage.

☐ If you are below the highest level of potential flooding, select a high-ground area to which you can move if flooding is imminent. Know how to get there in a hurry. Remember: many roads and trails parallel existing drainage patterns, and may be swept away by flood waters.

☐ If the emergency is a hurricane or flooding, bring in outside furniture, tools, trashcans, loose lumber, signs, garden tools, ornaments, toys, and hanging plants and tie them down or secure them. Harmless items become missiles of destruction in hurricane winds.

☐ Before the storm strikes, store drinking water in clean bathtubs, jugs, bottles, and cooking utensils. Your town's water system may be contaminated or damaged by the storm.

☐ Install storm doors and windows or other weatherproofing.

☐ Check your supply of home heating fuel.

★ ☐ **Move pets into sheltered, warm area,** such as a garage. Provide adequate food and especially water to last at least three days.

☐ Place large or heavy objects on the lower shelves of closets and storage areas. Brace or anchor high or top-heavy objects and wire or anchor overhead fixtures.

☐ Don't stack glassware or crystal. Take proper packing precautions to preserve their integrity.

★ ☐ **Bolt down or provide other strong support for water heaters and other gas appliances** since fire damage can result from broken gasoline and appliance connections. Use flexible connections wherever possible.

☐ Unsecured tall pieces of furniture, such as grandfather clocks or bookcases, should be put where they cannot fall easily, or braced, or put on the floor.

★ ☐ **It is very important to instruct members of your family on how to turn off water, heat, and electricity sources. This will help protect the home from backlash effects that often accompany a disaster.**

☐ Have on hand and be familiar with first aid handbooks, disaster relief handbooks, and other resource information that may be needed during an emergency.

★ ☐ **Photo inventory of home, garage, premises, other real estate holdings, and business.** Make a complete itemized list of and photograph or video tape all the contents of all the rooms in your home with items in their normal places. Include serial numbers, model number, physical description, where and when purchased, purchase price and estimated value. Attach receipts if you have them. You may want to use a tape recorder to record this information. Label all photographs. All personal or valuable belongings should be insured. This photo inventory should be in your kit at all times or in a safe deposit box at your bank. In case of a major loss, this should help you get a fast, fair settlement.

★ ☐ **"If time and room allows" checklist.** Compile a checklist of last minute items to do to prepare, or to bring along, such as family treasures, priceless antiques, etc. Several such items have been discussed in previous sections of this book. Post this list near the door or on the outside of your emergency kit.

AFTER AN EMERGENCY OR DISASTER . . .

1. *Exercise caution in entering or working in buildings that may have been damaged or weakened by the disaster.* They may collapse without warning. Also, there may be gas leaks or electrical short circuits.

2. *Don't take lanterns, torches, or lighted cigarettes into buildings* that have been flooded or otherwise damaged. There may be leaking gas lines or flammable material present.

3. *Stay away from fallen or damaged electrical wires,* which may still be dangerous.

4. *Check for leaking gas pipes* in your home. Do this by smell only. Don't use matches or candles. If you smell gas, open all windows and doors, turn off the main gas valve at the meter, leave the house immediately, notify the gas company or the police or fire department. Do not reenter the house until you are told it is safe to do so.

5. *If any of your electrical appliances are wet, first turn off the main power switch* in your house, then unplug the wet appliance, dry it out, reconnect it, and finally, turn on the main power switch. (Caution: Don't do any of these things while *you* are wet or standing in water.) If fuses blow when the electric power is restored, turn off the main power switch again and then reinspect for short circuits in your home wiring, appliances, and equipment.

6. *Check your food and water supplies before using them.* Foods that require refrigeration may be spoiled if electric power has been off for some time. Also, don't eat food that has come in contact with flood waters. Be sure to follow the instructions of local authorities concerning the use of food and water supplies.

7. *If needed, get food, clothing, medical care and shelter at Red Cross stations* or from local government authorities.

8. *Stay away from disaster areas.* Sightseeing could interfere with first aid or rescue work and may be dangerous as well.

9. *Don't drive unless necessary* and drive with caution. Watch for hazards to yourself and others and report them to local authorities.

10. *Write, telegraph, or telephone your relatives* after the emergency is over so they will know you are safe.

Adapted from *In Time of Emergency . . . A Citizen's Handbook*
by the Federal Emergency Management Agency, Washington, D.C.

Nuclear explosions cause intense light (flash), heat, blast, and initial nuclear radiation, which occur immediately. In addition, explosions that are on or near the ground create large quantities of dangerous radioactive fallout particles, most of which fall to earth during the first 24 hours.

Operation Teapot, Nevada, 1955. *Photo courtesy United States Department of Defense.*

ADDITIONAL EQUIPMENT

★ ☐ **Fieldbook** — Boy Scouts of America. Available at Boy Scout retail outlets.

★ ☐ **Emergency Preparedness** — Boy Scout merit badge pamphlet. Available at Boy Scout retail outlets.

★ ☐ **Wilderness Survival** — Boy Scout merit badge pamphlet. Available at Boy Scout retail outlets.

★ ☐ **Disaster Survival Handbook** — By Alton L. Thygerson, Ph.D. Available at your local bookstore.

★ ☐ *In Time of Emergency . . . A citizen's Handbook* (38 pages) — Available free from Federal Emergency Management Agency, Washington, D.C. 20472.

☐ *Outdoor Survival Skills* — By Larry Dean Olson.

☐ *Roughing It Easy* — By Diane Thomas.

☐ Booklet: *Preparing For and Responding To Emergencies: Guidelines for Church Leaders.* Available at the LDS Distribution Center in Salt Lake City, Utah.

★ ☐ **Master List of Your Kit's Contents** — In a waterproof plastic bag or laminated. Have it attached to or inside your kit.

★ ☐ **Plastic Bags and Ties** — All sizes.

★ ☐ **Heavy-Duty Garbage Can Liners and Ties** — 32 gallon type.

★ ☐ **Extra Zip-loc Bags**

☐ Portable Battery Operated Fan — To help keep cool.

☐ Flotation Life Preservers — One per person.

☐ Inflatable Raft and Two Paddles

☐ Collapsible, Portable Camping Stool

☐ Nylon Net Dunk Bag — Ideal for washing clothes and dishes or carrying gear in.

★ ☐ **Booklet: Essentials of Home Production and Storage** — Available at the LDS Distribution Center in Salt Lake City, Utah.

RECOMMENDED SUPPLIERS (1990)

EMERGENCY ESSENTIALS

Receive

Free Catalog

Features long-term storage foods, 72-hour survival kits, outdoor camping products, and first aid supplies! Write Emergency Essentials, Inc., Dept. F.E.P., 352 North State Street, No. B, Orem, Utah 84057. Or call toll free: 1-800-999-1863.

GRAIN COUNTRY

Features controlled atmosphere packaging of cereal grains (wheat, rice, rolled oats, etc.) and legumes (beans, peas, soybeans, etc.). A moisture-barrier laminated pouch (Flexible Can™) is vacuum-sealed for extended shelf life and inhibited bacterial growth.

Grain country also sells flour mills (hand and electric), bread-mixers, juicers, and other food preparation items. Shipping is available to all of U.S. and Canada. Ask for free information and price list.

66 North West State Road
American Fork, Utah 84003
(801) 756-9516 or Toll Free: 1-800-369-9516

K-TEC KITCHEN AND MACHINES

Wheat/Grain mills, bread mixing and food processing machines. A complete line of hand and power equipment to help you *store* and *use* whole grains every day.

Top-of-the-line hard Montana white and red storage wheat.

Call Toll Free: 1-800-288-6455 or (801) 222-0888.

K-TEC
370 East 1300 South (Space G)
Orem, Utah 84058
(In the Fred Meyer Shopping Plaza)

NITRO-PAK

Survival Food and Supplies

Carries year's supply food units (including freeze-dried and dehydrated), water purification and storage equipment, radiation detection equipment, books, videos, and more! 84-page catalog available for $3.00. Send to:

13243 East Rosecrans Avenue, Department BC-1
Santa Fe Springs, California 90670
Phone: (213) 802-0099

OUT N BACK

72-Hour Supply Headquarters

Complete selection of packaged 72-hour kits and Year's Supply units of air-dried and freeze-dried dehydrated foods as well as individual items for developing a supply designed just for you and your family's needs. For free monthly newsletter write or come into Out N Back, 7225 South 700 West, Midvale, Utah 84047 or Out N Back, 3067 North Canyon Road, Provo, Utah 84604. Both stores are open Monday-Saturday 10 a.m. to 6 p.m.

SAFEGUARD FOOD STORAGE & EMERGENCY PREPAREDNESS CTR

For free information on Food Storage, 72-Hour Kits, Water Storage, Wheat Grinders, Emergency Stoves, Lanterns, Flashlights, First Aid Kits, and other emergency products write to:

SAFEGUARD
463 South Main Street
Bountiful, Utah 84010
or call 1-801-292-1772

SALT LAKE PERMA PAK PANTRY SUPPLY STORE

See us for our complete line of food storage, bulk grains, 72-hour supplies, educational material. We have been satisfying customers for over 35 years. Mention this ad to find out about our free shipping offer.

2457 South Main Street
Salt Lake City, Utah 84115
(801) 486-4201 or (801) 486-4159
(Distributors of Perma Pak Food Storage &
"Ready-To-Go" 72-Hour Kits)

SI EMERGENCY FOOD AND EQUIPMENT

Receive Free Catalog

21 years' experience in the mail-order busines of providing everything needed to prepare your family for self-sufficiency. Catalog includes long-term storage food units, 72-hour emergency kits, retort food, as well as clothing and food for the outdoors. Write or visit our 15,000 foot showroom. SI Equipment, 435-B W. Alondra Blvd., Gardena, California 90248. Or call toll free 1-800-533-7415. Store hours Monday-Thursday 9 a.m. to 5 p.m. and Saturday 10 a.m. to 3 p.m.

STAT MEDICAL SUPPLY CO.

We carry a complete line of first aid supplies and medical equipment. Save time and money using STAT as your single source supplier for your total medical supply needs. Call or write to us for our free price lists.

STAT MEDICAL SUPPLY CO.
4555 South 300 West, Suite 500
Murray, Utah 84117
801-261-4363